Coincidence

50TH ANNIVERSARY EDITION

Luckii Ludwig

Coincidence

Murder at the Wild Idol Inn

50TH ANNIVERSARY EDITION

*Revised and Expanded with a
New Forward and Aftermath*

BY

Luckii Ludwig

Published by Byron Hot Springs *www.byronhotsprings.com*

EDITOR: Charleen B. Earley
BOOK COVER DESIGN BY: Leigh McLellan Design
INTERIOR DESIGN AND COMPOSITION BY: Maureen Forys,
Happenstance Type-O-Rama

About the Type
TEXT TYPE: Minion Pro, designed by Robert Slimbach, is inspired by classical, oldstyle typefaces of the late Renaissance, a period of elegant, beautiful, and highly readable type designs.

HEADS: Originially designed as Reporter by Carlos Winkow for the Wagner Foundry in 1938, the font was later upated as the slightly simplified Reporter No. 2. A bold and informal typeface, it works well as display type.

ISBN: 979-8-218-05110-5
LIBRARY OF CONGRESS CONTROL NUMBER: 2022945450

This is a work of creative nonfiction. The events and dialog are portrayed in the spirit and idiom of the time. While the events in this book actually happened, some names and identifying details have been changed to protect the privacy of the people involved.

10 9 8 7 6 5 4 3 2

For general information and reviews, please contact
historian@byronhotsprings.com
DISCLAIMER: All errors and omissions are the responsibility of the publisher.

Acknowledgements

R evising and reprinting a 50-year-old "true crime" story is not an easy task. Reprinting in facsimile would have been straight-forward, but there were updates and events that rippled through local history. The tragic events at the Wild Idol Inn have become the elements of local legend. People still reflect upon the tragedy today with implications for 21st Century society. They include the death penalty, criminal justice, the rule of law, and community safety and security.

For these reasons and more, a debt of gratitude for interest, encouragement and research are due. First and foremost, thank you David Spearman, the regular night Wild Idol Inn barkeep, who got the day off and lived to tell the tale. David stopped by the bar on that tragic night, noticed suspicious circumstances, did NOT try the door, went home and called the sheriff. He subsequently assisted the authorities in searching for the weapon, provided information useful to the investigation, and LIVED. He is the last person still living other than incarcerated prisoner, Virgil Gunther, with first-hand knowledge of that night's events.

The *Brentwood Press* reporter, Charleen Earley, recounted the 30-years distant Wild Idol Murders in her 2007 article. Today, she is a newspaper editor at *The Orinda News* and also writes for the *East Bay*

Times. Charleen reprises her 2007 article with a follow-up interview with the surviving, convicted murderer, Virgil Gunther, as a final update to this story. She also capably edits this anniversary edition.

Indefatigable researcher and genealogist, Magdalena Northcut, mined the Internet, find-a-grave sites, census documents, newspapers, obituaries, and queried prison administrative staff as part of this book. Thanks to her, we have insights into the effect these 1970 events continue to have on eastern Contra Costa County residents up to and including today.

Access to research materials provided by the Antioch Historical Society and the East Contra Costa Historical Society, and the *Brentwood Press* are gratefully acknowledged. Jacqueline Hanel provided the initial transcription and editing of the original *Coincidence* text from a 45-year-old facsimile photocopy. Finally, thank you very much to Barry Delavan, Officer (Retired), Antioch Police Department, for use of the Luckii Ludwig's personal copy of the 1st edition of *Coincidence* (Vantage Press 1977) upon which this 50th anniversary edition is based.

Contents

Foreword

The small rural town of Byron, located in far east Contra Costa County, sixty miles east of San Francisco, is not a likely setting for engaging historical tales. But as I discovered through my own research, sometimes sleepy little towns hold more intrigue than big cities. Such is the case for Byron, from its early history as a world-famous resort destination, to its home as a secret World War II interrogation center, to its locale of one of the grisliest murders in Bay Area history, Byron has stories to tell.

When Luckii Ludwig, a newspaper reporter in nearby Antioch, California was tasked with covering a triple murder in 1970, she could not have known the sordid details the police investigation would uncover. Through exhaustive research into police records, extensive interviews, and her own reporting, Ludwig recreated the scenarios leading to the gruesome encounters at Wild Idol Inn. *Coincidence* portrays the people, places, and events of that infamous night.

More than five decades later, one can learn about a senseless murder somewhere in the United States every day. These crimes may be related to societal inequities, gang affiliation, mental health issues, or sheer greed. Readers may debate the underlying reasons that lead to such violent acts, but it is difficult to know for sure just what causes an individual to take another's life. Through Ludwig's detailed narrative about the infamous Wild Idol Inn murders, so too can readers ponder what would cause two sets of individuals to engage in the same heinous act on the same night in the same place. Did some set of common underlying factors lead to the near-identical tragedies, or was it a Coincidence?

DAN HANEL
Author of the historical mystery
series, *In the Shadow of Diablo*
www.DanHanel.com

QR code for locating the Wild
Idol Saloon, Main Street,
Byron, California: longitude
37.8685, and latitude –121.64047
[*QR Droid*]

If the Wild Idol's Walls Could Talk, 2007

[Editor's note: This article is reprinted as it appeared in the Brentwood Press on April 7, 2007 with permission of The Press.]

I f the Wild Idol's walls could talk, they'd weave tales about its rich historical past of handshake business deals, fires and murders.

Last Friday, Byron's first saloon in 129 years began a new chapter in the town's history book as the doors re-opened to patrons in a wild way—beer flowed and the dance floor echoed the swoosh of the electric slide.

Street view of the Wild Idol Saloon 1971 showing fire damage [*East Contra Costa Historical Society*]

The bar closed in 1997 when it burnt down and was vandalized, and reopened briefly four years ago, offering just two days of drinking—call it a tease.

Open and ready for the next chapter, co-owners Bobby Botelho and Philip Weltin bought the landmark property in 1994, along with other buildings, soon-to-be restaurants, offices and more bars along Byron's Main Street.

Wendy Schilling of Discovery Bay and Carlos Owens of Byron, left, cut a rug *[sic]* at the newly re-opened Wild Idol Saloon in downtown Byron.

The Western-style tavern sports the original long bar and juke box, all stained-wood walls, fireplace, couches, flat-screen televisions along with a 72″ mounted above the bar, wall decorations from T.G.I. Friday's restaurant in Oakland, and side rooms with spittoons.

It's where 21st Century folk meet the Wild West, sans ghosts. Certainly not planned, the 2007 opening marks the 30-year anniversary of the book called *Coincidence*, written by Luckii Ludwig, which chronicles the three October 5, 1970 murders that took place at the Wild Idol.

Ludwig was a police reporter for the *Antioch Daily Ledger* when her editors put the Wild Idol assignment on her desk. Her 61-page book, available at the Oakley Library, gives a factual account in dialog about a no-name town of "600 people, if you count the cows," where several people's lives intertwine, coincidentally, at Byron's only bar.

The bar was built in 1877 by German immigrant Henry Wilkening, according to a chapter about the saloon in *Footprints in the Sand* by far East Contra Costa County historian, Kathy Leighton.

Henry Wilkening

Henry Wilkening (b. 1835 d. 1883), first resident of Byron and first postmaster. He established the first businesses in town: a hotel, boarding house, saloon, and livery stable as established in 1878. [*Illustrations of Contra Costa County with Historical Sketch, Smith and Elliott, Oakland, 1878 and Historic Union Cemetery: East Contra Costa County, 2020*]

The saloon was sold and renamed several times over the years, and in the late 1940s it was purchased by Louis and Pearl Crist. The Crist's renamed it the Wild Idol Inn, after one of Louis' favorite greyhound racing dogs.

After Louis' death, Pearl remarried and her new husband said he wouldn't interfere with her and her bar. She could run it as she pleased. According to Ludwig, Pearl stated that she, "Couldn't think of any reason to change the name."

The bar was her way of keeping busy. "Pearl liked the bar and the people who came in; she was at the bar during the day," wrote Ludwig. "She always had a big smile and a funny story to tell. She could listen or pass on as much gossip as the next person."

Then came the murders. While working at the Wild Idol one fateful evening, Bob Tracy, Pearl's bartender, age 65; his wife, Cecil, age 58; and Mr. Young, a father of four children, were shot in the back of the head. Pearl was on vacation at the time in Carson City, Nevada.

Ludwig, who is considering revising her original work, pieced her book together based on police reports and firsthand interviews with two of the five perps involved in the crimes.

"It took me about six months to organize and thrash through all the info I had in my notes, then about six months to write it. It took several years to actually get it published," said Ludwig, who now lives in Davis, California.

Five men were convicted of crimes and two of them, Willis Jones and Virgil Gunther, serve life sentences in prison for the actual murders. And while the murders were heinous crimes, there's been no evidence of spiritual activity in the bar since.

"When I finally went into that bar (years later), I didn't get any vibes like I had gotten from other cases," said Ludwig. "But if I hadn't known the bar's history, I never would have guessed anything bad happened there." Open for birthday parties, social events, wedding receptions (in their new park-like area), and to continue their fundraising events for such causes as Children's Hospital in Oakland, Neadle [sic] said, "The possibilities for the bar are endless."

"We'll have chili cook-offs, battle of the bands, bikini contests and bike runs," she said. "I'm on fire because there's so many things we can do with this place. It's not how much money we make; it's more about the memories!"

Business Card, The Wild Idol Saloon, 2015 [*The Wild Idol Saloon*]

Map of the San Francisco Bay Area indicating the location of Byron in eastern Contra Costa County with a ★ [*Mapquest*]

Located at 3918 Main Street, Byron, California. The Wild Idol's hours are Friday and Saturday from noon to 2 a.m.; Sundays till 11 p.m. Call (925) 240-9090.

CHARLEEN EARLEY, writer
The Brentwood Press
April 6, 2007

https://www.thepress.net/news/can
/article_cda23eaa-5a8d-5b58-a0d2
-9304e1cf667d.html Accessed on
November 1, 2022.

Street view of the Wild Idol Saloon February, 2023 [*Private Collection*]

A Few Words from the Author, 2022

I went to work as a police reporter for the *Antioch Daily Ledger*, the first week in October 1970, right after graduation from Marshall University, Huntington, West Virginia, with a Master's degree in communications. I also had worked for the *Lewiston Morning Tribune*, Lewiston, Idaho. I had never been to Antioch, California before my employment. The town seemed somewhat quiet and with a low crime rate consisting mostly of break-ins, thefts and family disturbances. A street gang had moved into the city next door: Pittsburg. I met their leader at the time, who assured me the gang members would not cause any problems, they just wanted out of San Francisco.

Imagine my surprise when I walked into the Antioch police station on Monday morning, October 5, 1970. There, an investigative police officer took me by the arm and said I was accompanying him to the Wild Idol Inn, Byron, to investigate a triple murder that happened overnight. I had never been to Byron.

I talked to everyone on the scene and gathered all the information available. When the officer and I returned to the Antioch station, two men had been arrested and charged with the murders. I talked to them in their cells, but all they did was scream and yell that they did not kill anyone! They claimed there were three other men who were responsible. As it turned out, they were right. They had kidnapped a man and left him at the Wild Idol Inn bar, but they did not kill him.

News of the murders swept the area. The murders even hit the San Francisco, Oakland and San Jose papers. People in Antioch did not talk much about the murders. However, once trials were scheduled, the town was abuzz with opinions about the death penalty. Many who opposed the death penalty definitely thought the two killers deserved the death sentence. In that end, Virgil Gunther and Willis Jones were sentenced to die. In 1972, California abolished the death penalty and 107 prisoners had their sentences reduced to life. These reduced-sentenced prisoners included Gunther and Jones.

Initially there was not much talk about the crimes. Everyone seemed stunned and at a loss for words. When the trials were set to begin, the talking started. People hoped they would get what they deserved although there was a lot of controversy over the death penalty versus life in prison. A member of one of the killer's family came to see me to express how horrible her family felt. Was there anything they could do? I told her to go home and pray.

Prior to coming to Antioch, I had worked for the *Lewiston Morning Tribune*. While working as a reporter for the paper, I had covered several murders, including a double murder. However, never did the idea of writing a book about any of them crossed my mind. Local newspapers covered these tragedies completely.

This triple murder at the Wild Idol Inn, Byron, was completely different from anything I had ever experienced in my life. Five perpetrators were involved, a man kidnapped and three innocent people shot in the back of the head. It was extremely stressful and difficult.

As a result, I dug into the story from every angle to try to understand how such a horrible crime could have been committed. I talked to family members of the victims, the perpetrators, friends and relatives, and neighbors in a desperate attempt to make some sense of it all. The editor chose not to publish most of my in-depth reporting, as he did not want to influence the investigation in any way.

After the murder trials, this book was created. Its purpose was, in part, to let people know as much as possible about the crimes, and partly to help clear my mind. My sleepless nights had to stop. Knowing all the details of what had happened troubled me a great deal. Revisiting this story is something I hoped I would never have to do. Never-the-less, there are people who do not know the story of the horrible tragedy that happened fifty years ago.

Vantage Press published the book initially. At that time, I did not have enough money to promote it adequately, so I never made any profit. That is fine—no regrets.

I left Antioch after two years of employment shortly after reporting these horrible murders and went to work for the *Contra Costa Times* in Walnut Creek, California. After three years as a reporter with the *Times*, I went into public relations with Western Electric, an engineering and manufacturing company in Berkeley, California. I never worked for newspapers again.

Since my days as a police reporter, a lot of people have gotten to know me. Most of them do not even know about my life outside of golf and my business. Working as a newspaper reporter did not pay very well at the time. To supplement my pay at the *Times*, I moon-lighted as a house painter. After hardly making any money on the *Coincidence* book, I decided to start a painting business. My dad taught me how to paint when I was in high school. Self-employment was a natural next step. I was a painting contractor for years in Davis, California, engaged in business as, "Women at Work." We did hire men occasionally, but most were women painters. I loved it because I could play golf, fish, hike and enjoy the outdoors. Retirement in 2005 allowed me to recreate all the time!

I no longer possess any supporting documents that even relate to these terrible events. At ten years to the day after the tragedy happened, I tossed away all of my notes and everything. No one had really spoken to me for years about the Wild Idol Inn murders and the coincidental circumstances that lead to the arrest of the perpetrators. I figured nobody needed anything more. I just threw all my notes, clippings and mementos away that day. Even my personal copy of the first edition Coincidence book went to a retired Antioch police officer six months ago. It is that last copy that provides the basis of this revised and expanded paperback edition.

Finally, I disclaim any stated or implied support in this *Coincidence*—50th Anniversary Edition regarding Virgil Gunther's innocence for the murders for which he was convicted or present fitness for release from the California Prison system.

LUCKII LUDWIG
September 15, 2022

Luckii Ludwig *Coincidence*
back cover jacket, first edition
[*Vantage Press 1977*]

Coincidence

Introduction

The morning was silent; even the roosters had not sounded their wake-up call in the early morning hours of Monday, October 5, 1970, in the small community of Byron, California, with a population of about 600, located in the east San Francisco Bay Area region, some sixty miles from San Francisco. There was only one bar in the town, the Wild Idol Inn, and it was to be the scene of a bizarre, unheard-of tale of kidnap and murder that hit the area like a bolt of lightning.

Many of the residents were already out in the fields working before three bodies were removed from the Wild Idol; three bodies were found face down on the floor, bullet holes through the backs of their skulls.

The series of coincidences and circumstances surrounding the murders led a prosecuting attorney in the case to comment, "This is one of the most grisly and horrible tales of crime and violence ever. The murders of three people in cold blood were a part of a week of crime and violence that these men were involved in before their apprehension brought an end to their violent acts. It is a sad commentary on our times when five men, committing such serious and separate crimes as kidnapping and murder, should meet by coincidence at the only bar in a small town and leave behind them three people murdered in cold blood."

Chapter 1

It was hotter than hell that first Sunday in October and Willis was tired. He was tired of having no money and of his wife's mother nagging at him. Betty's mother had been on his back all week about getting a job, paying his traffic fines, catching up on payments for the car, and buying a lamp for the house. "We aren't going to lend you any more money," she whined. "You're so damn lazy; I don't know why Betty ever married you. Pretty soon you won't have anything, not even a car to take me shopping in. Now, what are you going to do about it?"

Willis knew what to do; he'd leave the house. *No reason for me to sit around here in the heat and listen to that old bag,* he thought to himself. He'd go over to Virgil's. There would be peace and quiet there, anyway. As he drove, he thought, *Shit, I need that hundred and twenty dollars by tomorrow, or those fines will catch up to me, and then there's the car payments. And one thing I'd really like is to get away from this dump and that nag.* Then he remembered a conversation he and Virgil had earlier in the week with Todd Clair, a friend of theirs from Antioch.

"Hey," Todd had said, "I know this guy who'll buy cases of booze from us for fifty dollars a case, and I know some places where it's stored just waiting for someone to come in and pick it up. We can sell it, no questions asked, and make us a few bucks. Think about it you guys, and let me know."

Willis had looked for work all week, despite what his wife and mother-in-law thought. "There just ain't nothing available that pays anything, except hauling garbage, and there's no way in hell I'm going to do that. What the hell, you struggle all your life to get somewhere and then someone's always on your back because you never made it."

"Hi Butch," Virgil grinned as he let Willis in. "How you doing?"

"Pretty good, I guess, now that I'm here. Just had to get away from the house for a while, know what I mean?"

"Yeah, I know. I'd like to get out for a while myself. Things ain't going too good here either."

Virgil grabbed each of them a beer and they sat down at the kitchen table. "You know, Buck," Willis started, "I've been thinking about what Todd said about us being able to sell booze for fifty dollars a case. It sounds good to me, and we both can use the money."

"Yeah, but I'm a little worried about where we could get that much booze to make it worthwhile without getting caught."

"Hell, Virgil, Todd said he knew some places where we could go in and help ourselves, and shit, we could probably even rip off some bars. They store cases in the back. You know that."

"We'd have to be careful about hitting a bar with people in there," Virgil cautioned.

"Let's go see Todd. If we can't get to those places he knows, there are enough bars around here that don't do much business on Sundays. We could check them out any way."

Willis and Virgil left in Willis's 1965 Ford from Knightsen where they lived and drove the fifteen miles through Brentwood and Oakley to Antioch. They stopped by Todd's house to find he had gone to a party and wasn't expected back until later in the evening.

As they left Antioch, Willis said, "I know, let's go out to Byron. There's only one bar in town and they must stock up pretty good on the booze. The later it gets, the fewer people will be there, and Christ, there ain't even a cop in the town."

Chapter 2

The Wild Idol Inn was the only bar in the small rural community of Byron, a town of about 600, located in the East Bay region, fifty miles from San Francisco. Pearl Kelso had owned the Wild Idol Inn since 1949 and she had been working the day shift at the bar all those years. There had been many bartenders who helped with the night shift throughout the years. Old Jack Bernard had been her most steady and reliable bartender, but he retired. David Spearman helped as a relief bartender for nearly four years, but it was Bob Tracy who had come along and given Pearl her first opportunity for a vacation in a long time.

Bob was retired and getting along in years, but he felt a young sixty-five. He was a good worker and Pearl could trust him. Bob lived in the area before, but had recently remarried and moved back to Byron. His new wife, Cecil, was a dear. She was fifty-eight and worked part-time in a nursing home in Antioch. It was not uncommon to find her at the bar each night helping Bob clean up.

Business had picked up at the Wild Idol since Bob and his wife were at the bar. Everyone in the area liked them, and they liked their customers. Bob often played cribbage with some of the older men in town who'd stop by for a beer or two, and Cecil could often be found in the back conferring with one of the wives about a knitting stitch or some new recipe she'd tried. Their reliability started Pearl thinking about a vacation.

"Maybe I could finally take some time off. I need a vacation," she thought to herself. It had been her idea from the start to buy the bar. After her first husband had died, she decided she needed something to keep her busy.

Even when Pearl remarried, she kept the bar and her new husband left it all up to her to handle. "It's your bar; you run it the way you feel best. I won't interfere," he had said.

The Wild Idol had been a part of Byron's Main Street since 1900. At that time, the small community was thriving, destined to become a booming city. It was once even considered a possible state capital site! Sadly, after the river boom and mining declined, the town dwindled to a small core of farmers and ranchers.

The bar had been named by its first owner, an eccentric, rich old man. He named the bar after a greyhound race dog and Pearl couldn't think of any reason to change the name.

The Wild Idol hadn't been a big money-maker, but Pearl always came out on the long end of it and the bar made enough to merit keeping it. Besides, Pearl liked the bar and the people who came in; she *was* the bar during the day. People would stop in just to chat with her. She always had a big smile and a funny story to tell. She could listen or pass on as much gossip as the next person.

Pearl looked more like a member of the temperance union than a bartender. She seldom drank, but had fun working the bar and everyone in town loved her. But she wasn't getting any younger, so she was thrilled when Bob came back to work for her.

"I've decided to take off for a few days," Pearl announced. David said he'd work the day shift for her and Bob was more than happy to work nights because that shift was usually shorter.

By law, the bar was allowed to stay open until 2:00 a.m., but it was not uncommon to drive by at 11:00 p.m. or midnight and see the bar closed. "Don't worry about closing early," Pearl would say. "If there's no one here, or business is especially slow, or if you just plain get tired, close it up."

Before she left, Pearl took $1,047 in cash and checks to the bar to be used to operate the business while she was gone. "The cigarette man will be here Thursday, and the sandwich and liquor men will be here Friday. I've already ordered what I think you'll need, and the checks are made out for the right amounts. You should be set until next Monday when I'll be back. My God, that's the first Monday of October already. Where did the summer go?"

She always explained in detail things that people already knew, but Pearl just wanted to make sure things would be all right in her absence. "David will work the day shift; Bob, you'll have to be here at 9:00 a.m. to help him open. You're the only one with the combination to the safe, and I want you to take care of the money. Follow the same procedures. David will put the day's receipts in the cigar box in the ice chest, and you can lock it up with yours at night. Now don't stay open too late if nothing's happening, okay?"

"Fine, Pearl, now go and have a good time and don't you worry about a thing. We'll take care of everything at this end and we'll see you next Monday," Bob reassured her.

Chapter 3

E ven as Willis and Virgil were driving around Antioch, making their plans, Billy Vaught and Jimmy Dean were trying to escape the exceptionally hot October sun. They had never heard of Willis Jones and Virgil Gunther, and although they knew where the Wild Idol Inn was, they had never met Bob Tracy or his wife Cecil. In fact, they had met Pearl a couple of times, but never knew she owned the bar.

About all Billy and Jimmy cared about that hot Sunday was the heat. Normally, one could expect October to bring cool Indian summer weather with the leaves turning their familiar shades of red, orange, beige and yellow. Not this Sunday. Temperatures were more than 100 degrees Fahrenheit and the only colors noticeable were those of sunburns and mascara running down the faces of women looking for shade as they hurried down the street.

In some places, like Montana and Wyoming, there were snow-storms and travelers' warnings being posted as winter approached. Skiers were waxing their skis in anticipation of a long and promising season. Even Southern California was cooling down after a long hot summer that had brought what many called the worst brush fires in the history of the state. But what did those people know? Southern

California had been plagued by massive brush fires every year. In the aftermath, someone always called them the worst ever.

Someone had told Billy just the day before that it might rain by November. What the hell? Did he care? It wasn't raining now and last year it hadn't rained until December. It was cooler in San Francisco, he knew, but who wanted to go to the City on a Sunday afternoon? Funny, he thought to himself, even though Antioch was only about 50 miles from the City, the difference in weather was about as great as between a Berkeley hippie and a Bible totin' preacher. San Francisco always had fog, rain, or cool sea breezes. The Oakland hills, which weren't higher than 3,000 or 4,000 feet, stopped the cool breezes from floating over into the Diablo Valley. San Francisco was at least 30 degrees cooler.

The old timers, sitting along the San Joaquin River that flowed past Antioch, would sweat and swear at the hot October weather, commenting, "Won't be long before summer comes in January, February and March." Then they'd laugh as they thought of skiers on the slopes in July in 20 degree weather. Of course, they did admit they wouldn't live long enough to see the seasons change. Hell, they thought, no one would live to see the change, with all the pollution in the world. But they didn't care.

Antioch was a town of nearly 30,000 people if you fudged as the city officials did. There was little to do because it was too close to the big City to draw any main attractions. There were a couple of bowling alleys, lots of bars, and two movie houses with the same movies playing week after week… Going to a movie in Antioch was like watching last year's reruns on the late show.

Of course, you could always go to the city park and watch the teenyboppers freak out on drugs and then get busted by the cops. And there was the river, but if you didn't have a boat, all you could do was watch the patient generation propped up on a fishing pole, sleeping as the fish grabbed the bait and swam away.

One could always go down to the old Antioch bridge and wait for it to collapse. That was about the most exciting thing in town and from the regularity with which it was inoperable, it was about the only certain thing to happen in the community. The bridge had been standing since 1919 or so, but it hadn't been used much in the past few years. Spanning the San Joaquin River as part of the main road to Sacramento, the bridge had been out for a year because of floods. Then it was open for a year, until a ship hit it during a fog storm in September, one month before that fateful October Sunday night.

For Billy, Antioch meant a place to live and work, but it didn't mean much of anything else. It wasn't just Antioch; he would have felt the same about any place in which he lived. He'd lived in the area all his 28 years and had not been able to adjust to the nothingness he felt about the place or the hot weather that hit at unusual intervals. He didn't know much about city life and didn't care. He knew a little about the surrounding communities of Oakley, Brentwood, and Byron, but why know much about any other place? He'd be just as bored in some other town anyway. He could always call Jimmy and go have a few beers and shoot a game or two of pool.

"What do you mean Jimmy's not home? Where the hell is he?" Billy asked the woman on the phone. It didn't really matter, Billy thought; Jimmy was never home anyway. Of course, who would stay home when you lived with a bunch of women? He never could understand why Jimmy lived with his sister and her family when he had a wife living in Yuba City, but that was his business.

"Well, what store did he go to? Man, I don't want to go running all over town in this heat looking for him." Billy thought for a moment. "Listen, tell him to meet me down at the Hottertop when he gets back. I want to talk to him. Okay?"

Making a face into the receiver, Billy hung up and drove to the restaurant. As he sat there, he thought, "Me and Jimmy must be dumb to let women run our lives like they do. No wonder we have to get out every now and then just to have some peace and quiet. Women are always talking, always carrying on about something and always wanting you to do something for them, just 'cause you're there."

In his 28 years, Billy hadn't done much with his life, but then he couldn't think of anything to do that was really worthwhile. He hadn't held a steady job since the accident. Nothing ever went right for him; he never got any breaks, he thought. As a child, Billy lived in Oakley, a small town five miles east of Antioch. It wasn't much of a childhood. His family had enough to get by on and that was it—no extras, no frills. Billy had some problems when he was younger by seeming to be in the wrong places at the wrong times. There were a few minor juvenile offenses, but he never did anything serious enough to have a criminal record. Billy wasn't stupid, just lazy. He started high school and dropped out. He was bored with school and decided there must be more to do than sit around in a classroom. He hadn't been a discipline problem in school; he was just tired of it and quit.

One of his neighbors remembered Billy as "a nice, quiet guy, at least before the accident." Billy didn't drink when he was younger. He'd go to the bars and play pool, but drank sodas. He didn't like to fight. Part of his regular weekly schedule had been attending church with his family, but that had all changed.

"God damn head still hurts," Billy thought to himself as he took another sip of coffee. Severe headaches still plagued him at times, despite the fact that the doctor said they would eventually stop. At least they weren't as bad or as frequent as they had been.

"Damn that Anderson anyway," Billy swore under his breath. "If it hadn't been for him."

Billy's mind wandered back to Bruce Anderson. They had been close friends during their teenage years when either was in school. They used to play pool together and Billy would win because Bruce would drink too much beer and not be able to focus on the balls. They'd drive around in Bruce's car and pretend they were anywhere besides Oakley. They had welcomed in the New Year, 1961, and both hoped it would be better than 1960. It was the 4th of January. Anderson was driving as they left Antioch on their way back to Oakley, which had a new census figure for 1961 of almost 900, if you counted the cows.

Bruce was seventeen and Billy had already turned eighteen. "Hey, slow down," Billy laughed. "We're coming to Oakley. If you go too fast, you'll miss it." Bruce waved his cigarette and laughed.

"Well, we sure wouldn't want to miss this burg," Bruce said as his cigarette fell to the floor. He leaned down to find it and his eyes momentarily left the road. The car swerved and he lost control.

Billy yelled, "Look out, you damn fool." But it was too late. The car jumped a curb and struck a telephone pole on Billy's side of the car. The door and window came crashing in on him and Billy blacked out.

Bruce was treated for minor injuries and released from the Antioch hospital, but Billy hadn't fared as well. He lost a lot of blood and had a broken nose. That was the least of his worries. He hadn't remembered much about being in the hospital. He did remember Dr. Raymond Barker explaining to his mom, "He has some brain damage, and I don't know how serious it is. His mental capacity has been diminished to some extent and it may worsen. The only thing we can do is operate and place a metal plate over the area to protect it. If we don't, I am sure he will never be the same. It will, in fact, worsen with the years. The shield will save him and he should retain most of his mental abilities."

Mrs. Vaught hadn't liked the idea of a metal plate in her son's head, but realizing it was his only chance, she consented to the operation. Its use had not severely impaired Billy's judgment, the doctor said, but those who knew Billy knew he was never the same again.

Billy himself had doubts about the plate, especially when the headaches hit. They were worse when he was tired or if he drank too much. He had been in the hospital for six months and did not have a job although he was capable of working. Since that time, he had not been able to keep a job. "Don't know what's wrong with me. People never used to bother me. Seems like I'm doing pretty good on a job and then something happens. Someone says something and I get ticked off, blow up, and walk out."

Even Billy's marriage hadn't worked out. He had known Reba Lowe for years. They grew up together in Oakley, and Billy had thought for many years that he was in love with her. Somehow, the thought of being a father and settling down didn't appeal to him. They had married and three years later had a little girl, Heather Fawn. Billy smiled to himself remembering the day she was born. Reba had awakened him early in the morning. "Billy, I think it's time to go to the hospital. The pains are pretty frequent now."

"You mean you've been having pains all night?"

She nodded and he jumped out of bed, "Why didn't you wake me earlier?"

"It wasn't time yet, and you would have paced the floor and stewed about it. This way you got some rest. You have to work today, you know."

"To hell with work, my wife's having a baby," Billy shouted.

Despite all the excitement of having their first child together, it wasn't Reba's first baby. She had given birth to another daughter,

Machael Marie, two years before. She hadn't named the father. Billy wasn't sure he was the father and often fought with Reba about it. She claimed it was his child, and often this would start a fight between them. Then Billy would leave, looking for Jimmy and something to do besides staying home.

"Okay, boys, what's the trouble?" the bartender bellowed. "If you can't play a decent game of pool, then pack up and get out."

"You can't talk to us like that, can he, Billy? We come in here, pay good money for beer and pool and now you want to kick us out because two buddies are having a good time together."

"I ain't kicking you out yet. I just don't want things to end up in blows and one of you beating the shit out of the other."

Chapter 4

Billy had already finished another cup of coffee when he heard Jimmy's motorcycle roar up in front of the restaurant.

"Thank God he's here."

"Hi, Billy! What's up?" Jimmy grinned widely, revealing two missing teeth.

"Nothin', that's why I called. There ain't a damn thing to do. Thought maybe you'd like to have a few beers and shoot some pool."

"Well, I sort of promised my sis I'd be home for dinner and I have to stop and get some bread."

"What kind of shit is that? You're a big boy now, Jimmy. You can go out and do what you want. You don't got to be home at any special hour for dinner. Shit, tell her to get the bread herself. If you want to have a beer, let's go."

They hit several bars during the afternoon and finally stopped at Jack's for some pool. The beer was beginning to affect them.

"What do you mean, Billy? That was a bad hit. I saw it. You hit one of my balls before you hit your own. Come on, if you want to cheat."

"Cheat? Shit man, you're the one cheatin'. The only difference between cheatin' when you're sober and when you're drunk is you can't see as well when you're drunk, so you always swear I'm the one

Interior of Wild Idol Saloon Pool Room in 2022. The shades were down when the regular night bartender, David Spearman, arrived at 2:30 a.m. [*Private Collection*]

cheatin'. I get tired of playin' pool with you 'cause I have to spend so much time watchin' you instead of concentratin' on my game."

"Why you little…" Jimmy shouted as he went for Bill.

"Knock the shit out of each other?" Jack laughed. "Man, that's good. Me and Billy's never fought each other 'cause we're good friends."

Billy laughed, walked over to Jimmy and put his arm around his shoulder. Jimmy looked up at Billy, who was at least six inches taller and said, "Oh hell, Billy, let's go. This Jack bastard's going to be on our backs the rest of the day. Let's go somewhere else where we'll be appreciated."

CHAPTER 4

They walked out of the bar and Jimmy said, "Let's go to Brentwood on my bike. It'll be cooler than riding in your car."

"What for?" Billy asked.

"For a beer, that's what for."

"Okay, but let's park my car at Bejo's. It's on the way and we can come back there for a beer."

It was almost 10:00 p.m. when they rode up in front of Bejo's after the trip to Brentwood, but the night air was still warm. Sometimes, when the humidity was just right, the nights in Antioch were as warm as the days.

Jimmy parked his bike next to Billy's car. As they walked to the door, they spotted another man heading for the bar.

"Well, Mr. Young," Jimmy remarked, "what brings you out this late?"

"I had to go get some cigarettes and decided to stop in for a few beers. From the looks of you two, I'd say you must have had a few already!"

"Right you are, but then we don't have a wife and four kiddies at home to worry about," Jimmy laughed.

"Come on Mr. Goody Two-Shoes, we'll buy you a beer," Billy offered as they walked into the bar.

Chapter 5

It was that time of day when midnight makes the difference between two days. Willis drove up in front of the Wild Idol Inn. A pickup truck was parked in front and the lights were still on. The rest of the street was deserted. Willis and Virgil walked into the bar just minutes after the last customer, Mary Wilson, had left. She had been talking with Bob Tracy after having one too many drinks. "Suppose I should go pretty soon. I've already had too much to drink and you must be anxious to close."

"Yeah, the wife will be here pretty soon to help me cleanup. No use staying open if there's no customers."

Mary had just finished her drink when Cecil walked in. "Hi, dear," Cecil said, giving Bob a kiss on the cheek. "Where's everyone?"

"Just me here, Cecil, and I'm leaving. Have a good night."

Cecil started cleaning the glasses and Bob began wiping down the bar.

"Still serving?" Willis asked, sticking his head in the door.

"Well, we're just cleaning up, but we'll be here awhile if you'd like a couple of drinks. What'll it be?"

Willis motioned to Virgil, "Give him a scotch and water and I'll take bourbon and water."

The Wild Idol Saloon interior bar view, 2022 [*Doreen Forlow*]

Bob placed two glasses with ice on the counter and turned to grab the scotch and bourbon bottles. Willis carefully fingered the .22 he had under his jacket. Just as the bartender started to pour the drinks, Willis pulled the gun out and thrust it in his face. "All right, mister, put your hands out here on the bar."

Virgil pulled the .38 out from his jacket and pointed at Cecil who was busy washing glasses. "Get down there with your old man," he said nervously.

"Please don't hurt us," she pleaded.

"Just shut up and do as you're told and no one will get hurt," Willis answered, walking toward the windows and pulling the blinds shut.

"Where's the money?" Willis demanded.

"We don't have any except what's in the cash register. The boss was already here and took it home."

"You're lying," Willis shouted. He ordered Bob and his wife to lie down on the floor on their stomachs.

"Damned bartender pisses me off," Willis muttered as he and Virgil stood over them. He reached down and took Bob's wallet. "Keep those hands under your head," he ordered. Then he took the bartender's ring, watch and keys.

As Willis thumbed through the wallet, he said, "We're in luck; here's the combination to the safe." He knelt down by the floor safe and carefully worked the combination: 64 to the left, 27 to the right, 82 to the left, stop on 45.

"Wow, look at all of this," Willis said, handing Virgil some cash. There was approximately $800 in the safe. They grabbed the money from the cash register, but failed to look in the ice chest, where some $600 sat in the cigar box where the day bartender had left it.

"Watch these two, Virgil, I'll see if they have any booze stocked in the back."

Virgil stood over Bob and Cecil. Neither of them looked up, but Cecil was sobbing quietly. Bob lay there helpless and afraid to move to comfort his wife. His thoughts were mixed with hope that someone would come into the bar and with wishing the two gunmen would take what they wanted and leave. He knew there was no chance to get the guns away from them and he hoped that they would just walk out of the bar. He knew his wife was scared—hell, he was too but he thought to himself, *They don't look like the type who would hurt anyone.*

"Yeah, but what are we going to do with it? We got no place to put it and we don't even know where to sell the stuff," Virgil quipped.

"I know. We got to go get Todd. He should be home by now."

"You mean drive back to Antioch and then come back here?"

"Sure, why not?" Willis answered. "There's no cops out here. It's late, no one's around and everyone thinks the bar's closed. We can leave the door unlocked and come back."

"But what about these two?" Virgil said, waving his gun at Bob and Cecil on the floor.

"Oh, yea, well, we can't very well take them with us. We'll have to leave them here."

"Yeah, but..."Virgil cut in.

"Shut up, Virgil. There's only one thing to do. We got to come back and get the rest of the stuff here," Willis said, kneeling toward Bob.

"No, no, no," Cecil screamed, "Please don't hurt us. We won't tell anyone, please let us go."

Bullet riddled blue, 1965 Ford Mustang get-away vehicle as registered to Willis Jones. Spectators counted 28 bullet holes. [*John Wilson, Antioch Daily Ledger*]

"Shut up, broad," Willis shouted, pointing the gun to the back of her head. He squeezed the trigger and her screams stopped as her head thumped against the floor.

"You dirty son of a bitch," Bob shouted as he tried to move for Willis.

"Get him, Virgil," Willis yelled at almost the same time as another shot rang out from Virgil's gun.

Then there was silence. Willis and Virgil looked at each other for a moment, paralyzed. "Let's get out of here and go get Todd," Willis broke the silence.

They left the bar on the run and jumped in the blue '65 Mustang waiting outside. They sat there for a minute, breathing heavily. They looked up and down the street, and seeing no one, they left and headed for Antioch.

Chapter 6

Billy, Jimmy and Mr. Young continued drinking at Bejo's. Young was a department head in a local grocery store. He was a quiet man, but he liked to drink and was well known in many of Antioch's bars. He would go in, have several drinks, never saying much and never causing any trouble. Then he'd leave and go to another bar and drink some more. His wife and four children were at home. He had worked on that hot Sunday and then was greeted by some of his wife's relatives who had come over for dinner. Later in the evening, he felt he had to get out for a while and have a couple of beers, so he told his wife he was going out for cigarettes. He didn't plan to be gone long.

Young excused himself from the bar at about 11:00 p.m. as Billy and Jimmy kept drinking. He returned at about 12:30 a.m. and sat back down next to them.

"Man, you are smashed," Billy laughed as Young had some difficulty getting on the bar stool. "Where in the world have you been? You were fine when you left here."

"Oh, shut up. So I've had a few. No law says I have to sit here and drink all night."

Jimmy answered, "Okay, okay, don't get upset. We was just wondering how you managed to get so bombed, that's all. We been drinking all day and we ain't bombed yet."

"The hell you're not. Anyone in this bar will say you're both drunk!" said Young.

"Wait a minute," Billy cut in. "I don't drink very much, you know that. It gives me a headache."

"Well, then it must be those pills you are always taking."

"Hold on, old man. Are you saying I'm a pill head? 'Cause if you are, I'm going to knock your head off. You know I don't touch no stuff like that."

"Oh no? Then what is it that you get so high on?" said Young.

Jimmy stopped the argument. "Lay off him. Billy has to take some pills 'cause he ain't well, but he never took nothing he wasn't supposed to, and I know that for a fact."

"Thanks, Jimmy," Billy muttered.

"Don't pay him no mind. Young has a big mouth when he's been drinking."

The three sat, drinking in silence until the barmaid, Gidget, called for last rounds. "OK, gang, drink up. We close in fifteen minutes."

"My God," Jimmy said, "is it that late?"

Young finished his drink and left without a word. Billy and Jimmy gulped theirs down, glanced at each other, and then walked out behind Young.

"Hey, Mr. Young, where are you going?" Billy yelled as they walked toward his car.

"Home, I've got to work tomorrow."

"Listen, why don't you come drinking with us for a while?

We won't be gone long and we'll bring you back to your car. Come on, just to show there's no hard feelings."

"It's 2:00 a.m. All the places are closed," he answered. "We can get Gidget to sell us a six-pack and we'll drink that. What do you say?"

Young let go of the door handle and walked over to Billy and Jimmy, "Sure, okay, why not?"

Jimmy went to the back of the bar and knocked on the door. "Hey, Gidget, it's Jimmy. How's about getting us a six-pack to go?"

James Dean (left) and Billy Vaught at arraignment, Delta Justice Court [*Doris Connally, The Brentwood News, October 16, 1970, page 1*]

She opened the door, saw Jimmy standing there, and went and got a six-pack. Jimmy gave her the money and muttered, "Thanks, see you later."

Taking the six-pack under his arm, Jimmy walked back to Billy's car and the three of them got in. Billy started the engine and rapped out the pipes. His car sounded as though it needed a tune-up and a muffler.

They drove around, drinking, laughing and sharing stories of stupid things they had all done when they were drunk. "Shit, we're almost out of beer," Jimmy said, opening the last can. "Got any money on you, Young?"

"No, I don't."

"Well, hell, we can't quit drinking now," Billy put in.

"We're just getting started, and I'll bet we can find another place to get some beer. Right, Jimmy?"

"Right, but we got no more money."

"Well, that's really OKAY, guys. I got to be getting on home anyway," Young said.

"What do you mean, go home? Thought you were going to drink with us."

"I did and now we're out of beer, so I better go. Why don't you take me back to Bejo's?"

"Wait a minute," Jimmy said. "Seems to me that Billy and I bought you a few beers at the bar and then I bought this six-pack. So it seems it should be your turn to spring for the beer."

"But I don't have any more money on me and it's late. I'll buy you guys a beer next time I see you."

"That don't seem fair now, does it, Mr. Young? Maybe we should stop somewheres and have you call your wife and have her bring you some money so me and Billy can keep on drinking. That would be fair, wouldn't it?"

"No, I don't think she'd go for that. Maybe we better just forget it for tonight. I'll catch you later."

"Forget? Hell, we ain't going to forget," Billy shouted.

"You said you was going drinking with us. We did our part in getting some beer, and now it's your turn. And, who knows, maybe we'll want something to eat later, so how about it, Young, got any money around your house?"

Young sat there silent, thinking, and then commented, "Listen, I've got an idea. Let's stop somewhere and I'll call her and see if she can bring us fifty dollars or something. You guys can borrow it and keep drinking if you like, and I'll go on home."

They were near 18th and D Streets in Antioch and Billy and Jimmy sat there, neither saying a word after Young's offer. Then Billy spotted a telephone booth. "Okay, there's a telephone down there by the grocery store. You call your wife, Young. That store stays open all night and maybe we can talk the clerk into selling us some beer. It can't be much past 2:30 a.m. You tell your wife we need fifty dollars right now. Don't tell her it's to go drinking or she might not bring it. Tell her you've been kidnapped or something," he laughed. "She could even come with us if she wanted to," Jimmy offered.

"I don't think she'd want to. She doesn't drink much. "I'll just call her and have her bring the money down here. Then I'll give it to you guys and you go on without me. She wouldn't want me to go."

"Listen, big man," Jimmy said, grabbing a hunting knife from under the seat and waving it at Young's face. "This was your idea. You're calling your wife and getting that money so all of us can go drinking. We aren't ready for you to go home yet."

"Well, I'm not going and that knife doesn't scare me.

I'll get the money and you guys can have it," Young said from the back seat.

As they drove up in front of the store, Young reached over the front seat and grabbed for the knife in Jimmy's hand. Jimmy turned quickly and caught Young under the chin with the knife, opening a small cut that started to bleed. Young took another grab for the knife and tried to find the door handle.

The sight of blood startled both Billy and Jimmy and then it incensed them. Billy stopped the car and yelled at Young, "Look you fucker, if you don't want to get hurt bad, you better sit back and do as you're told. You got us mad now."

Jimmy looked in the store and saw the clerk looking out at the car. "Let's go," he said, turning back around in the seat and holding the knife in front of Young, who now moved back in the seat, uncertain of what to do next. Billy drove out of town a ways and asked, "What do we do now?" "I don't know, but this little punk pisses me off. Why don't we teach him a lesson? Let's stop and call his old lady and tell her that her dear, sweet, loving drunk husband has been kidnapped, and if she wants the precious little thing back, it'll cost her fifty dollars. Then we can take the $50 and leave Young to his old lady. We'd have more fun without him anyways."

"Yeah, we would at that. The sight of him's starting to make me sick. Hey, Young, want to call your wife now and have her come out and rescue you from the big bad guys?" "Why don't you guys leave my wife out of it? She's probably sleeping. Take me home. I'll get you some money and then leave me alone."

"Oh, come on now," Jimmy put in, "wouldn't it be more exciting to call the little woman? She's probably waiting up for you, or is she used to you staying out all night?" Billy thought for a minute, "There's a telephone at that gas station at Highway 4. It ain't too far from here. We could call his wife from there."

"Sure," Jimmy agreed. "Then we could have her meet us out here somewhere. Know a good place?"

"Yeah, there's a little town up the road, and it's easy to find. There's only one bar in town, so she could meet us there. From there it ain't far to Stockton and they have places that are open all night."

"Great, let's call her, and hey, we could call her from the bar."

"It's closed. Besides, it will take her a while and if we call from here, we won't have to wait at the bar so long."

"Okay, what's the name of the bar?"

"The Wild Idol Inn."

They stopped at the telephone booth and Billy said, "Okay, Mr. Young. You can either get out nice and quiet to call your wife, or Jimmy here can give you a hand, not so quiet." Jimmy grinned, showing his missing teeth.

"I'm not calling my wife. I don't want her to be part of this. You guys are sick."

Jimmy put the knife closer to Young's throat, grabbed his arm and pushed him toward the phone booth. "Okay, Young, what's your number?"

Billy found the number in the telephone book as Young stood near the booth in silence. He put a dime in and dialed the number.

A sleepy voice at the other end muttered, "Hello."

Billy whispered to Young, "Tell her you need fifty dollars. Just let her hear your voice, then I'll talk to her."

Young took the phone, "Honey, I'm in trouble, these guys are crazy."

"What kind of trouble? Lloyd, where are you?"

Billy grabbed the phone, "Mrs. Young? You love your old man?"

"Yes, yes, I do. Who is this?"

"Never mind, just listen. Bring fifty dollars to the Wild Idol Inn in Byron in thirty minutes, if you want to see your husband alive again.

"But I don't know where Byron is or the Wild Idol Inn."

"Just bring it."

"I don't have any cash. Can I bring a check?"

"Don't be silly, lady; bring the money in thirty minutes. Your husband will be sitting in a car outside the bar with a friend of mine. I'll be in a place where I can see you and everyone else coming into town, so don't call the police. We have a two-way radio and we'll be able to hear the police calls. If you really want him back, be there with the money."

"Is Lloyd alright?"

Billy put his hand over the receiver, "Convince her we mean business. Tell her we have a knife on you and you're bleeding."

"Honey, they have a knife at my head," Young said.

"That's right, lady, and blood is already gushing from his head, so hurry," Jimmy shouted into the receiver.

Billy put the phone close to his mouth and said, "Okay, thirty minutes at the Wild Idol Inn."

They walked from the phone booth, pulling Young with them. Billy laughed, "Christ, we really scared your old lady. She thought we were serious. Hell, who'd want to kidnap an old fart like you? Well, she'll be sure to get the money to us now, no problem."

They put Young in the back seat and headed for Byron. "Now, let's go and sit and wait at the Wild Idol Inn. Too bad they won't be open, we could have a beer while we wait," Jimmy laughed.

Chapter 7

Willis was a year younger than Virgil, and he was taller, slimmer, and better looking. They often got together because they had a lot in common; neither of them worked regularly. Willis took odd jobs here and there when they came up or when he was desperate for money. He enjoyed jobs like moving mobile homes or driving some type of vehicle.

Willis wasn't dumb; he just acted instead of thinking at the drop of a hat. He had a certain charm and tact. He had a short temper and could blow up at the drop of a hat. He had a certain charm and tact about him that usually enabled him to get what he wanted.

He was single when he first met Virgil, but married Betty about ten months after Virgil and Sharon were married. After their marriages, Willis and Virgil grew even closer. They spent more and more time together, away from home.

Willis never had a problem getting girls, and while he liked them for the most part, they were a burden to him, tying him down and keeping him from doing the things he liked to do. And he liked being alone at times.

He had been bored in school, not because he couldn't understand or because he was too far ahead of the material. Willis failed to see what good an education would do him out in the world. He didn't care whether he learned math and English.

When Willis decided to marry, his friends weren't sure whether he was marrying because of his love for Betty, or because it seemed like the thing to do. She was the logical choice. They had known each other for several years and seemed to get along well together. Willis was never dependent on Betty and, because he had always fended for himself, she often felt she was only a convenience in his life.

Willis was the only male of seven children. His father was drunk most of the time. And when the family lived in Illinois, Willis would go off by himself to escape the arguments and rampages of his father. He joined the Army as soon as they would take him. When he was stationed in Korea, his mother died. He was eighteen when he came back from the service to try and keep the family together. Relatives took the three youngest children while Willis and two sisters moved to California.

Willis had never been in serious trouble. His major offense was the accumulation of several traffic tickets in neighboring San Joaquin County, most of them for speeding. Somehow, his Mustang was always going faster than the signs along the road permitted. Willis never paid any of the tickets and the interest was accumulating against him.

He had worked in Tracy, San Joaquin County, the month before and had paid some of the fines. Time was running out on paying an additional $120. He was to report back to the court on Monday, October 5th.

After he left the court, Willis had helped move some mobile homes and stopped off at Joey's, a small bar in Tracy. The bar was nearly empty; only the barmaid and one other customer. So Willis played a few games of pool with her. He left after losing three straight games.

CHAPTER 7

On his way back to Oakley, Willis stopped in to see his sister Donna and her husband Frank Delgado. Willis and Frank had a couple beers and then headed for Virgil's house.

"Hey, man," Willis had said when he saw Virgil, "Frank here has a great idea. Remember how the other day we was saying we'd like to go up to Tahoe, but we didn't have the money? Well, Frank knows this guy who lives in Oakley, and he's got all kinds of stuff in his house. He doesn't even lock the front door. Frank says he's so dumb that even if he was missing something, he probably wouldn't think of reporting it to the police. Wanna go with us? We can sell the stuff and pick up some bread."

Virgil thought for a minute, "Yeah, I'd like to, but what if we get caught?"

"Jesus, Buck, ain't no way we're going to get caught. Come on now, don't disappoint us."

It was dark as they drove past Alfonso Garcia's house. "Good, he's not even home. Not a light on in the whole house," Willis noted.

They parked the car in front of the house and sat there for a few minutes. Seeing no one on the street, Willis motioned for the others to follow him. The door was unlocked and they walked in. Willis pulled out a flashlight and the three began rummaging through the house.

"Let's get out of here," Virgil whispered, "We've been here too long. The old man might come home. Besides, we ain't going to find anything in here."

"Get a hold of yourself. We ain't hardly looked yet. And what's your problem? Don't you think you're due this? You don't got a chance anyway. Nobody likes you. You got a record. You're broke and don't know where you're going to get any bread. Don't you think they owe you?"

"Sorry, Butch, but I get a little nervous. I just want to get out of here."

Frank found some money hidden in a drawer and they helped themselves to the booze in a cupboard in the kitchen.

Before they left, Willis grabbed a shotgun and two pistols.

They each came out with fifty dollars apiece. Frank took most of the booze and Willis kept the guns. It hadn't been profitable, but as Willis pointed out, "It's better than nothing." Later that week, Virgil and Willis went to Antioch to the 639 Club for a few beers. When they walked out, Willis said, "Did you see that guy in there flashing that roll of bills? Man, he must be loaded."

"Yeah, I saw. Sure would be nice to have all that."

"Well, we can. He's so drunk and he doesn't seem to be all there anyways. You know, kind of touched in the head. He probably drives a nice car too. We could borrow his money and the car and go to Tahoe. Go get that gun out of my car and we'll wait for him. Come on, we can have a good time on his money."

They didn't have to wait long until Jesse Mahaffey staggered out of the bar and walked to his car. "Got a match?" Willis asked.

He looked at Willis and Virgil and without saying a thing, started to open the car door. Willis grabbed him and shoved the gun in his side. "Get in and move over. My friend's going to sit in the back with this gun. You say anything or do anything and he'll blow your head off."

They took Mahaffey's wallet and drove the back roads to Brentwood and Knightsen and then down Holland Tract, an area used by fishermen along the San Joaquin River.

When the car stopped, Mahaffey spoke for the first time, "What you guys going to do with me?"

"Shut up and get out. Virgil, get that rope off the floor and we'll tie him up. Just be cool, mister, and you won't get hurt. We're going to borrow your money and your car for a while."

They left Mahaffey lying on the ground, tied and scared. It didn't take long to drive to Tahoe and even less time to lose the two hundred dollars they found in Mahaffey's wallet. "Well, we might as well head back. That guy's money didn't last long," Willis laughed.

"Oh, well, easy come, easy go," Virgil chimed in.

They picked up Willis's car in Antioch and drove both cars to Brentwood.

"What we going to do with this car," Virgil asked as he climbed out and walked to Willis's car.

"Shit, I don't know. We don't want to be driving it too much. Why don't we set it on fire?"

"Why?"

"Why not? We ain't got nothing better to do."

It was nearly morning when Willis let Virgil off at his house. He yelled, "Hey, Buck, it's Sunday. I'll be over later and we'll do something. Maybe we can have another good time and make more money this time, okay?"

"Yeah, see ya later, Butch," Virgil answered. "Hey, you ain't going to church or anything today are you?"

Chapter 8

Virgil Gunther had never known a father. His dad died when Virgil was eight, and for six years, he had only his mother. She remarried when Virgil was fourteen, but by that time, he had learned to live without the help, advice, discipline and love of a father. He resented the outsider. If Virgil had any hopes of getting to know his stepfather, they vanished with the man's death when Virgil was nineteen.

Being overweight most of his life, Virgil was subjected to being called names by his peers, and was rejected from many circles. He wasn't violent or hateful toward those who abused him. Instead, he quietly withdrew into himself, trying to make friends and please those who showed an interest in him. Virgil had one scrape with the law at the age of nine: he stole a lawnmower. His mother was working and trying to make enough money for them after his father died, so Virgil decided he could help by mowing lawns. The only problem was he didn't have a lawnmower, so he stole one. Virgil was reprimanded and the lawnmower returned to the owner.

In his early days, Virgil was sympathetic towards other people and animals, partly because he received no sympathy himself and he understood the plight of others. But in later years, bitterness replaced that sympathy. One day, when Virgil was a child, a stray dog followed him home from school. Virgil thought it was cute and was going to ask his mother if they could keep it. The local dogcatcher; however, picked the dog up because it was loose on the streets. Virgil watched with apprehension and felt so sorry for the dog that he let it out of the truck. Since it was impossible to know which kennel his dog was in, Virgil opened all the kennels. Happy in their newfound freedom, the dogs followed Virgil. The group was not hard to follow and the dogs and Virgil were caught.

Virgil later caused excitement around the house after his mother remarried. He was expelled from school at the age of fifteen for participating in a dice game. Always seeming to need money as he grew up, and never having any, Virgil discovered he could get money by forging checks.

Alabama lawmen caught him, and Virgil spent two years in prison.

When Virgil was released from jail, he and his mother moved to Knightsen. He remained anonymous until September 1969, when an Antioch woman reported her 16-year-old daughter missing, and having last been seen with Virgil.

The mother had filed a missing-person report on Sharon Morse. Such reports are generally considered routine and police can do little but record the information and notify authorities in neighboring cities. Sharon was supposed to have gone to school the first day of the term; she never showed up at school and she didn't come home.

In an area such as Antioch, which lies close to a large, metropolitan area like San Francisco, missing teenagers are not uncommon. They leave home for many reasons and travel to the big city, hoping to be caught up in its vastness. San Francisco, which houses the famous Haight-Ashbury district, and the Fillmore area, offers a haven for teenagers who feel the establishment of home closing in on them.

Many young girls run away from home to get married, convinced it is the answer to what seemed an unfavorable and undesirable home environment.

Her daughter had last been seen with Virgil Gunther, a twenty-two-year-old unemployed laborer. They were seen in Brentwood the day Sharon disappeared in a 1955 faded blue Chevrolet. But she was not satisfied, and she called the *Antioch Daily Ledger* to tell her story.

Sharon's mother notified officials in San Francisco and Reno, the marriage capital of the West Coast. She also notified friends and relatives of both Sharon and Virgil that the girl was missing.

Unless there is a reason to suspect foul play, missing teenagers were usually not reported in the Antioch paper. However, Sharon's mother handed over a picture of the girl and sobbed out a story to a reporter who decided to make a feature out of the incident.

"Won't you come home?" the mother sobbed through the printed page. "She's scared to come home; I know it, but everything will be all right if she just comes home. I'm worried sick about her. She's only sixteen. He's not a teenager; he's an adult."

That's when the story ended as far as the paper was concerned, but it was learned that Sharon and Virgil had been married in Reno on October 5, 1969.

Sharon and Virgil came back to Knightsen and moved in with his mother. It was easy for the three of them. Virgil seldom worked and his mother, Estelle, tried to make enough for all of them. Often she and Sharon argued about the household duties.

Sharon's mother never forgave Virgil for taking Sharon away from home to marry before she finished high school, and amongst all the family squabbles, Sharon and Virgil were having problems. Sharon, immature in years, and Virgil, immature because he had never been forced to grow up, were both mothered by Estelle. They seldom went anywhere together and Sharon was left alone, complaining that Virgil saw more of Willis than he did of her.

Chapter 9

Todd Whitson Clair had moved to Antioch in the middle of July 1970. He remembered the day clearly because it was one week before his eighteenth birthday, July 26. He had left Red Mountain, California, telling his relatives he was going to Antioch with a friend to find work.

Clair hadn't worked steadily in Red Mountain and found that his lack of education hurt his chances of finding a good job, but he didn't like the idea of going back to school. He had always found ways to get money. One sure way was to burglarize homes. Eventually, Clair got to know enough of the "right people," so that he could fence almost anything. But a couple of burglaries had been sloppy and he had almost been caught, so he decided to move on.

Clifford McCleary and Todd moved into a small five-room duplex, along with John Robertson, a friend of Todd's. Shortly after his arrival in Antioch, he met Willis, through another friend, Ray Peterson.

One day, the three of them were sitting at Todd's house when he commented, "You know, if things don't start happening around here, I'm going to have to break down and find a job. I don't have a cent left."

"What did you do in Red Mountain for bread?" Willis asked.

Before he could answer, Ray butted in, "Are you kidding? What did he do? Hell, he never worked, that's for sure. He used to go around to people's houses, visiting when they weren't home, and take things, huh Todd?"

"You don't say," Willis Jones laughed. "Well, just maybe I can help you if you're interested in pulling a couple of jobs. I've been known to pick up a little spending cash myself that way, and we both know old Ray here's been around."

That had been the start of their friendship, and it was Todd who said one night, "Listen, I know a place in Porterville where we can sell hot booze for fifty dollars a case. If you know of any places, let me in. I know a couple of warehouses where the stuff just sits around waiting for someone to come in and take it."

The day after Willis had been in court in Tracy about his fines, he and Virgil dropped in to see Todd. He had the .22 he had taken from the house in Oakley the night before. "Hi, guys. Come on in. Want a beer?"

"Sure," Willis answered. He pulled out the .22. "How do you like my new gun?"

"Looks okay," Todd said, holding it in his hand. "Where'd you get it?"

"Oh, we picked it up at some guy's house last night. Want to shoot it?"

They went out to the backyard and set a bottle up in a box. Todd took a couple of shots at it and one of his roommates shot it a few times. "Not bad at all, for the price," Todd had laughed.

On that hot, first Sunday of October, Todd had gone to a party with some friends. When he and Cliff came home, they were both feeling no pain. "Well, at least it has cooled off enough. We should be able to sleep tonight."

"Yeah, oh, Todd, don't forget you said you'd wake John up at five. He starts that new job tomorrow."

Todd went into the bedroom, set the alarm for 5 a.m.

He pulled off his shirt and trousers and crawled into bed. Todd was awakened by a loud continuous pounding at the door and he couldn't ignore it. The sound kept getting louder. It wouldn't stop. He looked at the clock next to the bed but he couldn't focus on it. A small pain was developing over his right eye. "Shit, what's that noise? Is it my head pounding or someone at the door?" he thought to himself. He got up and slipped on the trousers he had carelessly thrown on the floor, and went to the door.

"Hey, man, get up. We got lots to do," Willis greeted him.

"What's up?"

"Well, you said you knew a place in Porterville where we could sell booze for fifty dollars a case, didn't you? Well, we know where we can get plenty. Come on, we'll show you."

"Sure, sure, come on in while I get ready. Just give me a minute," Todd said, noticing the .22 Willis had tucked in his waistband. Virgil had a gun tucked in his pants, too, but it didn't have a pearl-handle grip like Willis's.

Todd walked into the kitchen and picked up a couple of beers, and threw them to Willis and Virgil, and then opened one for himself.

"Here, have a wallet," Willis said, tossing him a worn-out dark wallet. Todd caught it and walked into the bedroom. He laid it on the nightstand and looked at the clock. It was 3 a.m.

They left the house and Todd asked, "Where we going?"

"To a little bar in Byron. It's all set; nothing to it. We can take all the booze we can get our hands on."

Virgil laughed, "Yeah, it's just like someone left the door open for us."

"You with us?" Willis asked.

"Sure."

"Think you could kill someone?"

"I don't know."

"Well, if it really came down to having to kill someone, could you do it?" Virgil asked.

"I really don't know. Guess that's something I'd have to decide at the time. Why all the questions?"

"Well, we've already snuffed two," Willis commented. "We got some money out of the safe. That guy just pissed me off when he wouldn't open the safe. Said the boss had already taken it home."

It was nearing 4:00 a.m. when they arrived in Byron and drove down the street. There was one other car on the street, a white Ford with a black primered hood. Willis drove up to the bar and reached under the seat. He pulled out a pair of gloves and put them on. He got out of the car and walked across the street to watch the Ford, which was driving up and down the street. The car stopped in front of the bar next to Willis' car.

Willis walked across the street as Jimmy got out of the car. "Hi, what brings you out here tonight?" Willis asked.

"Oh, nothing much, just a little business to attend to."

"Can't be legitimate business at this hour. You planning to knock off this bar or something?"

"No, no, really. We're sort of waiting for someone."

"Well, wait somewhere else. We're taking care of this bar."

"Well, no, you see, we can't do that. We sort of kidnapped this guy and we're waiting for his old lady to bring the ransom money out here, that's all."

Willis laughed, "You guys kidnapped someone and you're getting ransom for him? Why in the hell did you pick this spot?"

"Shit man, we don't know; it just sort of happened that way."

"Oh, that's good, that's really good."

Virgil and Todd got out of the car and walked over.

Billy sat in his car with Young. "What's happening?" Virgil asked.

"Oh, these dudes kidnapped this guy and they're waiting for the ransom," Willis chuckled.

"How much did you ask for?" Virgil snickered.

"We just needed fifty dollars to go drinking with," Jimmy answered.

"Fifty dollars? Beautiful. Shit, you could just steal one case of booze and make that without all this trouble," Willis said.

"What do you mean?" said Jimmy.

"Oh, never mind. Might as well come on in with us and wait for your ransom to arrive, if it's going to."

"Is the door open?" said Jimmy.

Virgil walked over and turned the knob. The door opened and Jimmy motioned for Billy to come on in.

Inside, Willis threw a set of keys to Todd. "These should open the pool table and the cigarette machines. See what you can get out of them." Todd got the machines open while Billy and Jimmy grabbed cigarettes and sandwiches. Virgil rummaged through the purse on the bar.

Willis jumped up on the bar and grabbed a sword display above the bar next to the picture of John F. Kennedy. When Willis and Virgil took Todd to the back room to show him the cases of booze, Jimmy shouted from the front. "Hey, this is a bar. Anyone want a drink?"

Willis ran out to the front and pushed in front of Jimmy. "Sure, let me mix them. I always wanted to be a bartender." He stepped over the bodies behind the bar and said, "Well, what'll you have?"

He began pouring drinks and noticed Young standing by the pool table, silent. Todd was carrying cigarettes and booze to the car, while Billy was loading up his car with sandwiches and other items from the bar.

"Hey, mister, you want a drink?" Willis yelled to Young.

"Huh? Oh, no thanks."

Todd was about to go out with another load of booze when he thought he heard a car. He put the cases down, ran to the window, and looked out, but he didn't see anything.

He took the cases out to the car. When he walked back in, Willis was at the end of the bar picking up a plastic vodka bottle that stood nearly three feet tall and was three-quarters full of pennies. "Here, take this to the car," he motioned to Todd.

Todd walked around to the end of the bar. He reached for the bottle and then looked to the floor. He saw the bodies of a man and woman lying face down. Both were lying in a pool of blood. Todd stood frozen for a minute. He took the jar of pennies and hurried out the door. He made one more trip to the car when he heard a car door slam. He looked and saw Jimmy and Billy in the white Ford. They started the engine and sped away. He put the liquor in the car. All of a sudden, he heard a loud noise like a gunshot. He jumped around and saw Willis running out of the bar, putting his gun into the waistband of his pants. He looked for Virgil and saw him opening the other door.

"Come on, let's get out of here," Willis ordered.

They all jumped in and raced out of town. Todd thought that he had spotted a police car on the way in as they were leaving, but he tried not to think about it; he just wanted out of Byron.

"Can you imagine kidnapping a guy for $50? Well, he saw too much. We couldn't have him hanging around," Willis said as he drove toward Antioch.

When they arrived at Todd's, Willis and Virgil walked in and sat down. They took their guns out and laid them on the table. Todd went to the kitchen for a beer. All three of them jumped when the alarm went off. It was 5:00 a.m. Todd went in and shook John, "Hey, it is time to get up."

Todd finished dividing the money he had taken from the bar and Virgil pulled out a roll of bills.

"Wow, that's a lot of money. Where did you get it?"

Willis flashed another big roll and said, "Oh, we got it at the bar earlier."

They unloaded the beer and put everything in Todd's garage. Willis handed him the jar of pennies. "Why don't you hold onto these too and we'll divide them later."

Todd put the pennies in his closet. Willis and Virgil went home and went to bed. Todd finished his beer and sat on the couch thinking; then he went to bed.

Chapter 10

The early morning hours of Monday, October 5th, were busy for the Antioch police. Besides the routine drunk and family-disturbance calls that usually plagued the department during the weekend, an eighteen-year-old youth had shot and killed his mother's boyfriend during an argument.

Earlier, officers answered one call at the apartment after the boyfriend bloodied the mother's nose. The boyfriend was arrested at that time on a warrant, but he was released and returned to the apartment. He argued with the youth. Suddenly a gun appeared and in the struggle over it, the man was shot.

Police were just cleaning up most of the big calls and getting ready for the start of a new week, when a call came in from a clerk at the all-night grocery store at 18th and D streets. It was 2:40 a.m. The clerk reported three men in a 1965 white Ford with a black primered hood had been in front of the store. One of the men had a knife.

An officer was dispatched to the store. "You Milton Troutman?" he asked. The clerk nodded. "Well, tell me what you saw."

"Well, this car drove up in front, a 1965 Ford, or maybe a 1966. Anyway, it was white and the hood on the car was black primer. Here's the license number, I wrote it down. So, there's these three men in the car. I didn't think too much about it at first, but then

1966 Ford Mustang with Black Hood, facsimile 2022. Not actual vehicle [*Classic Cars.com*]

I noticed they was arguing or struggling about something. One of the guys in the front kept pushing the one in the back down on the seat. Then I see a knife pointing at the guy in the back. They saw me looking and drove off."

"Did you see which way they went?"

"They headed out on D street."

"Anything else?"

"No, sir."

The officer climbed back into his patrol car and radioed in, "I'm coming back in."

"What was that all about?" the dispatcher asked.

"Oh, I don't know; the clerk claims he saw two men holding another at knifepoint in the back seat of a car. Better check out the license number and get back to me."

Headline News [*The Brentwood News*]

A few minutes later the answer came back from Sacramento that the car was registered to a Billy Dwayne Vaught. "Why don't you alert all units to be on the lookout for the car, just in case there might be something to it," the officer related to the dispatcher.

"Attention, all units. Report of a man being held at knifepoint at Short Stop Market at 2:40 a.m. Victim with two male suspects in a 1965 white Ford with a black primered hood. License number DZM 084, registered to a Billy Dwayne Vaught, 25-A Sunset Drive, Antioch."

Shortly before 4:00 a.m., the dispatcher answered a call from an upset and distraught woman who identified herself as Mrs. Norma Young, 500 Shaddick Drive.

"My husband's been kidnapped. He called and said they are holding him for fifty dollars ransom at a bar in Byron called the Wild Idol Inn. What do I do?"

"Try to keep calm, Mrs. Young. I'll send an officer out to your house right away."

"Oh, hurry please," she pleaded. "They said they'd kill him if I didn't get the money to them in half an hour."

Lt. Leonard Reed was at home asleep after a busy weekend. He was the senior officer on call for the weekend. "Reed," the dispatcher said, "We just got a call from a Mrs. Young at 500 Shaddick Drive who says her husband was kidnapped. That address is close to you. Better get over there on your way to the station. We're sending another officer out too."

Reed climbed out of bed, dressed and drove to the Young residence. Mrs. Young was crying and hysterical when he arrived. Several of her children were up and she had already sent one of them down to her sister's to borrow the fifty dollars she needed to get her husband.

"He left about ten last night to get a couple of beers and some cigarettes. I sat and watched television and then dozed off. When I woke up, it was past 2:00 a.m. and he wasn't home yet, so I took my son's car and went looking for him. I drove to Bejo's because he goes there and it's the closest bar to the house." She started to cry and then regained her composure. "Well, the car was there but the bar was dark. I went up and looked in the window, but I couldn't see anything. There was a motorcycle parked near the door, but nobody was around or on the street anywhere. I looked in the car to see if he had fallen asleep, but he wasn't there either. I figured he had gone with some friends to get something to eat."

Mrs. Young told Reed she had gone to sleep and was awakened by the phone call. "It was silent on the line for a few seconds and it sounded like a bad connection. Then Lloyd came on and said he was in trouble and he was being held hostage for fifty dollars. A younger man took the phone and said I was to have the money at the Wild Idol Inn in Byron in thirty minutes, or ..."

"That's okay, Mrs. Young. Try to relax. We'll handle it." Reed sent an officer to the apartment of Gidget, the barmaid, to see if Young had been in the bar earlier. She told the officer that two men named Billy and Jimmy had been in the bar and were drinking with a third man named Young, but the third man had left before they did.

Then Reed called Antioch's only policewoman, Martha Frye. "Martha, Reed here. Get to the station as soon as possible. You're going to Byron with a woman whose husband has been kidnapped. We'll meet you there in a few minutes."

Antioch police alerted the sheriff's department, which had jurisdiction in the Byron area, and then called the police in neighboring Brentwood.

At the police station, plans were being made to deliver the ransom. Units from Antioch and the sheriff's department were rolling to Byron to stake out the bar. Policewoman Frye and Mrs. Young were to drive in the Young's station wagon to deliver the money. However, Mrs. Young was crying and so upset, they decided she should not go out to Byron. Police decided the kidnappers probably did not know Mrs. Young anyway, so Mrs. Frye could go. The Young's son, Monte, asked to go with the policewoman, so the 18-year-old and Mrs. Frye headed out the main road to Byron.

Reed and Officer Jerry Oliver, in an unmarked car, took the back road, hoping to reach the bar before the Young's car.

Sheriff's units had already arrived in Byron and surrounded the bar. A unit from Brentwood arrived and covered the rear entrance to the bar. One of the deputies, noticing the lights were still on in the bar, made his way to the front door. He moved to the front window and gazed through the slats in the blinds. He thought he saw a man and a woman lying on the floor behind the bar. It looked as though there was blood on the floor around them. Then, he heard a coughing noise and fell to the ground, not aware that what he had heard was what is often referred to as a "death rattle," the result of air passing through the body of a dead person. He crawled to the other window and looked in. There was a man lying on his stomach between the pool table and the door. He wasn't moving.

The officer scampered back across the street to the patrol car just as Antioch police and Policewoman Frye entered Byron. "There's three bodies in there on the floor. It doesn't look good. I heard somebody cough, but I didn't see anyone else in there.

The officers moved in closer to the front door. Six of them crashed through the unlocked door, guns drawn. The bar was deathly silent and empty, except for the bodies on the floor, blood drying on the backs of their heads. Machines were broken open and parts lying around on the floor, cigarettes and papers were scattered about, a woman's purse sat on the bar. The door to the safe was open and there were glasses partially filled on the bar. A sword, bent out of shape, lay on the floor near the door.

Chapter 11

Lt. Reed had taken the back road to Byron, driving past Bejo's, where officers earlier had retrieved the Young's station wagon. As he drove past, he noticed a white Ford parked in front of the bar. He made a U-turn and came back, noticing the black primered hood. He checked the license number with the one given by the clerk at the all-night grocery. It matched.

One man was in the car and another was straddling a motorcycle parked near the front door. "Let's get them!" Reed shouted as he sped into the parking lot and slammed on the brakes. "You take the one on the bike," he yelled as he jumped from the car.

Both pulled their service revolvers and Reed said to the driver, "Get out of the car and take your driver's license out, slowly."

"What's wrong officer? If there's been any trouble, we don't know nothing about it. We just got back from Concord," he said, pulling his license out of his wallet.

Upon verification that they were Billy Dwayne Vaught, age 28, and James Dale Dean, age 24, Reed opened the door of the car. The back seat was loaded with sandwiches, beer, cigarettes, and other items. Reed read them their rights and told them they were under arrest for suspicion of burglary and possession of stolen property.

Reed called into the station, "Yeah, this is Reed. I'm at Bejo's. We have two suspects in that kidnapping in custody, Vaught and Dean. Send a unit out to impound the car. There's a lot of stuff in the car and it looks hot. Any word on Young? He's not with them."

The dispatcher was silent for a minute and then he responded, "Uh, Reed? We just got word in from Byron. They found Young and two other people at the Wild Idol. They're, uh, dead, all of them, shot."

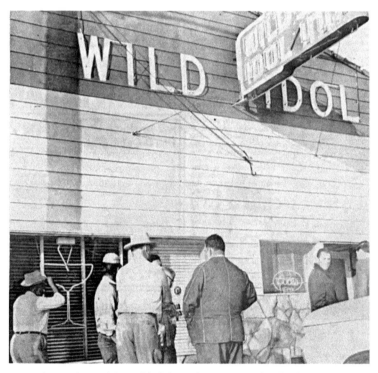

Bystanders in front of the Wild Idol Inn the morning after the three murder victims were found. Deputy Constable, Stanley Pereira in denim jacket with his back to the camera along with Antioch Police and County Sherriff Deputies investigating the scene. [*Antioch Daily Ledger, October 5, 1970, page 1*]

"Oh, my God! Get that unit out here fast. We're going on to Byron."

By the time Reed arrived in Byron, lab crews were already combing the bar for fingerprints and other clues. Mrs. Frye ran up to him, "It looks like Young, the night bartender and his wife in there. They're all dead. I have the Young's eldest son with me. He hasn't been told anything yet, but I'm sure he has it figured out."

"Where is he? I'll talk to him, then the two of you better head back to Antioch."

They walked up to the station wagon where Monte was sitting. "My father's in there, isn't he, isn't he?"

"Monte, this is Lt. Reed of the Antioch police."

"My dad's dead, I know, so why don't you tell me what's happened?"

Reed looked at him, "I'm sorry, son. It appears that your father and two other people have been shot. We really don't know too much yet, but we do already have the two men in custody that he was with earlier."

"I want to go in. What kind of a son-of-a-bitch would do such a thing? What'd my father ever do to them? He wouldn't hurt anyone. I'm going in there."

"Monte, I think it's best you stay out here. I'm sending you and Policewoman Frye back to Antioch. You'll be needed there more."

By 8:oo a.m., most of the details had been sorted out, with two suspects in custody and the three victims identified. Vaught and Dean were yelling there were three others involved who had done the killing, and police were trying to find out what the two had done with the rest of the loot that was missing from the bar. And there were no other weapons found in Vaught's car except a hunting knife that had bloodstains on it.

During all the commotion at the police station, a woman walked into the station to inquire about her brother, Jimmy Dean. She was quickly whisked off to Mrs. Frye's office.

"My brother's name is Jimmy Dean. He didn't come home all night and I'm worried about him. He said he was going out for a few beers yesterday afternoon and would be home early."

Mrs. Frye looked at her, "Wait here just a minute. We do have some word on your brother. I'll be right back."

"He's not dead or hurt, is he?"

"No, no, he's alive, but he has been arrested. Let me get Lt. Reed."

Dean's sister sat back in the chair. "Oh, no, I hope it's nothing serious. His wife is supposed to be moving down from Yuba City this weekend," she thought to herself. "What could he have gotten himself into; he's not that bad, a little inconsiderate, maybe, but …"

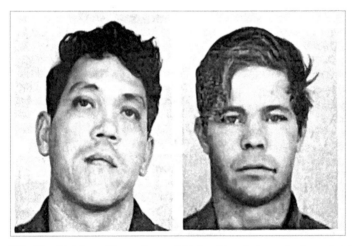

Billy Vaught, left, and James Dean, right, booking photographs (mug shots) [*Antioch Daily Ledger, October 7, 1970, page 1*]

Her mind drifted back. Jimmy had left his wife in Yuba City and come to Antioch to find a job. Things had been slow; the upholstering business hadn't been lucrative. But now his wife was coming to Antioch. They hadn't lived together much in their four years of marriage. Jimmy had gone in the service right after they were married.

She remembered some of the stories he told her. "Man, I was happy in Yuba City. Things were quiet, not much doing. We'd have a few beers and a few girls, but the Army, it was different. Pot, pills, sex, everything and anything you wanted was more than plentiful."

Jimmy had flipped the Army off when he walked out after being discharged. "It was like getting out of jail," he used to say. It had been the happiest day of his life and he got so drunk he couldn't stand. He'd lost his dinner for three days after that, swearing he'd never drink again.

Lt. Reed walked into the room with Policewoman Frye.

"You're Jimmy Dean's sister?"

"Yes, where is he? Is he in trouble?"

"I'm afraid so. He's being held here on charges of burglary, kidnapping, and murder."

"Oh, my God, no, no, not Jimmy," she began sobbing. "He wouldn't do such a thing. Can I see him?"

"Not right now, but would you mind answering a few questions?"

"Not at all, if it will help."

"Does he drive a motorcycle?"

"Yes."

"Could you identify it if you saw it?"

"I think so."

"Would you consent to go with one of the officers to identify it? As soon as things settle down here we'll let you talk to him."

"Okay, but I just can't believe it. There must be some mistake."

Chapter 12

Pearl Kelso was up early Monday morning. She had a long drive back to Byron. She quietly packed her suitcase and said good-bye to her friends, thanking them for making her first vacation in years a real treat. As she drove down the road, she turned the radio on and then off again. It was a beautiful fall day in Nevada. She wished she didn't have to return, but she had business to attend to.

Pearl called her husband Friday to say she'd be driving back Monday morning instead of Sunday afternoon. Bob had told her about the 100-degree weather they were suffering through. She didn't rush the normal four-hour drive back. She relaxed and enjoyed the view and the fall colors. She had left some cleaning in Stockton and decided to pick it up.

"I hope they haven't given it away,"she thought to herself. "It's been three weeks since I took it in."

"Hi, I'm Pearl Kelso, I believe you have some cleaning for me, if you haven't given it away," she laughed.

"Oh, yes, Mrs. Kelso, we sure do. We were wondering when you'd be in. It's been several weeks since you were here."

The clerk went to the back and picked up the clothes. "That'll be eight dollars and twenty-three cents. What brings you out today?

I figured with all the excitement in Byron, you'd be over there. You do still live there, don't you?"

"Yes, I do, why?"

"Well, with those murders and all, did you know any of them?"

"What murders? I've been out of town for a few days, haven't heard a thing."

"It's been on all the radio stations this morning. Three people were shot and killed in some bar in Byron, and they already have the two guys that did it."

"Who was killed?"

"Don't really know much about it. Apparently, some bartender at the bar and his wife were killed, along with some man the two guys had kidnapped."

"You say this happened in a bar?"

"Yeah, at some bar in Byron."

"My God!" Pearl exclaimed. "I own the only bar in town." She ran out of the cleaners and jumped in her car and headed out of town. She couldn't believe it. There must be some mistake. Not the Wild Idol. It had to be somewhere else. She reached down and turned on the radio. She was almost to Byron when the noon news came on.

"Here's a late news bulletin about that triple slaying in the small town of Byron in East Contra Costa County.

Antioch police have tentatively identified those three persons found shot to death as Lloyd Young, age 40; Robert Tracy, age 65, night bartender at the bar where the killings occurred; and his wife, Cecil, age 58. Police report they have two men in custody in connection with the murders, but no formal charges have been made. Items believed stolen from the bar were found in the suspects' car when they were apprehended early this morning. Stay tuned for further bulletins as we receive them."

Three Silhouettes, *Coincidence* front cover jacket, first edition [Vantage Press 1977]

"Oh, no," Pearl sobbed. "It just can't be. Not that dear man and his wife." Tears came to her eyes. "Why?" She thought about Cecil and the first time they met. She had thought Cecil was an odd name for a woman, but she and Mrs. Tracy had been close. "She was always so good about helping Bob clean up at night."

Still not believing what had happened, Pearl drove into Byron and down Main Street. It was packed, people were everywhere. Several police cars and an ambulance were parked outside the bar. She got out of the car and walked numbly towards the bar. "I'm Mrs. Kelso. I own the bar," Pearl said, introducing herself to an officer at the door. "What happened?"

"Well, it seems three people were killed here early this morning. We just took the last one out. Why don't you leave your name and number with the officer in charge and go on home? There's nothing you can do here now, but I'm sure they will want to talk to you later."

Pearl nodded and wrote down her name and phone number for the officer, and dazed, climbed back into her car and drove home.

Chapter 13

As the press began putting its story together, bannering it across the front pages of many East Bay newspapers, three persons were sleeping in anticipation of a busy day.

Willis was up early and asked his mother-in-law, Melba Hobbs, to drive him to Tracy. He was scheduled to appear in court to pay the remaining $120 in traffic fines at the justice court. He paid cash and left. Then she drove him to Brentwood to Dasher Motors. He paid $210 in cash for back payments on his Mustang.

Later that day, Willis and Betty stopped by to pick up Virgil and his wife. Virgil's mother was going to follow in her car later and

Headline News! 3 persons murdered at Byron [*Antioch Daily Ledger*, October 5, 1970, page 1]

asked directions to Todd's house so she could join the party. The occasion was Willis's birthday and Virgil's first wedding anniversary. Donna and Frank Delgado were already at the party when the others arrived. The women sat in the living room talking, while the men wandered back and forth to the kitchen, making toasts and telling wild stories.

"Hey, Todd," Willis yelled, "Go get the pennies. We should divide them."

Todd picked up the heavy Vodka bottle and took it to the kitchen table. "Where did you get all those pennies?" one of the women asked.

"That's our little piggy bank," Virgil laughed.

"Hey, why don't we pack up the party and go to Virgil's?"

He's got lots of penny wrappers and they'd be easier to divide," Willis suggested.

The party moved to Virgil's and a blanket was spread on the floor. The women sat and helped count and roll them. It was taking so long that the men got restless, so they went to a local bar to play some pool.

"I'm a little tired," Todd said. "Think you could drop me off at home?"

"Sure, but what about your pennies?"

"Oh, bring them by tomorrow. I just don't feel too good."

Willis and Virgil took Todd home and stopped by the liquor store to get some more beer. "Pick up a couple of papers, Virgil. We can read about ourselves," Willis laughed.

When they returned to Virgil's apartment, the women had just finished rolling the pennies. Willis sat on the couch and read the account of the murders out loud to everyone. "Hey, we ought to try that," Virgil commented. They both laughed.

CHAPTER 13

Early Tuesday morning, Willis took $25.67 in pennies to Todd's and then went to the bank in Brentwood. He deposited $109, including $20 in pennies. Todd buried his share of pennies, along with the wallet Willis had given him. Then he bleached his hair.

Chapter 14

Pearl Kelso and Louise Drayer had something in common, even though they didn't know each other; they both owned bars. Pearl's was the Wild Idol Inn, the only bar in Byron. Louise's bar was located about 20 miles from Byron, in San Joaquin County, near Tracy.

They were similar in looks, with two pool tables and a long narrow bar with bar stools around it. Pearl's bar sold both liquor and beer, but Louise's only sold beer and wine. Neither bar was crowded often and both could be found closed early at night if business was slow. Neither bar had a history of trouble because they were both located in small communities and owned by people in those communities who knew most of their customers. No one was a stranger in either bar; both women were generous when it came to buying a drink for a stranger.

Pearl didn't play pool, but Louise, who played often, was good. She beat most of the male customers who'd challenge her. She was working the Tuesday night after the killings in Byron, but business was slow.

Willis picked up Virgil that Sunday evening and they went for a drive. "Why don't we head over to Tracy? I know a nice little bar over there. We can have a few drinks and play some pool," Willis suggested. It was after midnight when they pulled into the parking lot at Joey's.

Louise was pouring a draft for the two customers, Curtis Long and Bob Fox, when Willis and Virgil walked in. The only other customer that night was Jim Nichols, and he was leaving as Willis and Virgil drove in. Fox came in early in the evening to play some pool, and Long came in after bowling to see if he could do better at pool than he had at bowling.

Willis walked up to the bar, "How about a couple of beers? Coors."

"Sure, Louise said, reaching for the beers. She looked at Willis and recognized him. "You out moving mobile homes again?"

"No, not tonight. Just decided to come in for a beer." Fox and Long were playing pool while Willis and Virgil sat at the bar, watching. Then Willis got up and went outside. He returned a few minutes later and sat back at the bar. Louise looked up and then continued washing glasses and cleaning behind the bar. As soon as they all left, she planned to close. She was placing some glasses on the counter when she heard Willis say, "Okay, this is it." She turned around and stared down the barrel of a gun. Virgil was holding a gun on Fox and Long near the pool table.

Willis moved Louise from behind the bar toward the pool table and ordered all three of them to lie down on the floor with their heads on their hands. He put on a pair of gloves while Virgil took wallets and watches from the three helpless people on the floor.

Virgil looked at one of the watches and threw it to the floor, "This one isn't worth a damn."

Louise, her voice shaking, asked, "Can I keep my watch, please. It was my mother's." Virgil left the watch on the floor.

Willis walked over to the windows and pulled the drapes shut. Then he started turning out lights and pulling plugs to the jukebox and cigarette machine. He walked to the other window and flipped a switch so the Coors-signs lights would go out, but nothing happened. He shrugged and walked toward the cash register. He pulled out all the money, stuffing it in an empty peanut box. "Hey, Louise, this all the money you got?"

"Yes, that's it, just what you find in the cash register." "Bullshit! If I find any more, Louise, I'll kill you." Scared, Louise told him her purse was in a drawer next to the cash register and there was money in it. "Where's the safe?"

"It's in the back, but there's no money in it."

Willis walked over to her and helped her to her feet, "Well, why don't we just go see about that."

Louise grabbed the keys from behind the bar and headed for the storage room where she kept the safe. She put the key in the lock to open the door when Willis noticed the front door open slightly. He headed toward the door. "Drop it," a voice commanded. Then the words were repeated, "Drop it." Jones let the gun slide to the floor and stood motionless.

Louise looked over at Virgil sitting on a stool with a gun aimed at the front door. "There's another one in here!" she shouted. Jones dove to the floor, grabbing his gun as the front door closed.

"Back off, or I'll blow your head off," Virgil shouted across the room.

Units from Tracy and San Joaquin County had surrounded the bar after deputies had been alerted that a silent alarm was sounding at Joey's. Without knowing it, Willis had accidentally tripped the alarm when he was turning off lights in the bar.

Virgil checked out back to find police all around the building, so he took Louise to the front window, "When I pull back the curtains, you wave out there and tell them to go away or we'll kill you."

Byron Deaths, Tracy Holdup
Linked in 2-County Probe

Missing Loot, Time Gap, Guns Puzzle Police

By LUCKII LUDWIG
Ledger Staff Writer

ANTIOCH Daily LEDGER

THE EAST BAY'S BUSY / INDUSTRIAL CENTER

Single Copies 10c; Per Month $1.50   ANTIOCH, CALIFORNIA   FRIDAY, OCTOBER 9, 1970   48 Pages   Vol. 100, No. 200

Headline—Tracy and Byron Crimes linked, Luckii Ludwig, staff reporter, on the job [*Antioch Daily Ledger, October 9, 1970, page 1*]

Louise could see police crowded in the parking lot as she waved. "Please go away. There's three of us in here and they will kill us if you don't leave."

No one left the parking lot. Virgil broke the window "Tell them again. Maybe they didn't hear you."

Louise yelled again as one of the deputies shone a light on her, "Please go away. There's three of us in here and they'll kill us if you don't leave."

The officers, who had been joined by units from the Highway Patrol, backed out of the parking lot. The phone rang in the bar. Startled, Willis answered it without thinking. "Hello, yeah, it is. Who's this? Well, what do *you* want? Are you crazy? We have three hostages in here. We aren't surrendering. Sure, we'll deal about them, but not to give ourselves up. You think about it and come up with something better or we kill them," Willis shouted, slamming the phone down.

Louise moved back behind the bar. "Hey, Louise, since you're back there, how about a couple of beers while we wait?"

She got a six-pack from the cooler and set it on the bar.

Long and Fox were standing near the pool table and Fox called out, "How about us? We have to wait, too?"

"Sure, help yourself. They're free. You give them a beer, Louise, and keep track of what I owe you. I'll pay you when I get out of jail."

After several calls from the sheriff, Jones announced, "Okay, we're set. We leave them here unharmed and they will back off and not follow us."

Willis and Virgil darted out the door, into the car and sped off down the road. Willis checked the rear view mirror. No one followed them. However, several police units were waiting up the road and took after the speeding Mustang as it turned down a county road. Jones drove through a roadblock set up at one intersection while officers shot at the car. One of the tires was hit and the car went out of control, sliding across an empty field.

Officers converged on the car and found Jones lying beside the car, his head grazed by a bullet. Virgil was cowering a few feet away. Both were arrested and read their rights.

Chapter 15

News of the "copycat" attempted robbery in Tracy sent Antioch police scurrying to see if there were any link between it and the Byron slayings. A .38 caliber revolver, a shotgun, and a .22 revolver were found with Virgil and Willis after the Tracy hold-up. The guns matched those stolen in Oakley in September and were the same type used in the killings at the Wild Idol Inn. A combination to the safe at the Wild Idol was found in Willis's wallet. It was the same written combination Pearl Kelso had given the bartender before she left.

With these new developments, Willis and Virgil were charged with the same crimes as Billy and Jimmy had originally been charged with, and an all-out effort to locate the fifth man, was started. A week later, Todd was arrested at his home. He voluntarily turned over the pennies and the bartender's wallet Jones had given him.

Before any of the five could appear for a preliminary hearing, they were arraigned on charges of murder, kidnapping, robbery, conspiracy to commit theft, burglary, and possession of stolen property. All entered pleas of not guilty and preliminary hearing dates were set.

Bullet riddled blue Ford Mustang showing passenger side door open. The shot gun was one of many weapons found inside the car when Wilson and Gunther were arrested. [*John Wilson, The Antioch Daily Ledger*]

By editing statements made by Jones and Gunther after their arrests, a superior court judge ruled they could be tried together and set their trial for January 11, three months and six days after the murders.

With Jones and Gunther labeled as the "trigger men" in the triple slayings, the district attorney's office decided to prosecute them first, hoping answers to the degree of guilt on the part of the other three would be decided. Todd turned state's evidence to avoid being tried for murder.

The story of the crimes were fitting into a bizarre account of several separate crimes being committed on the same night in the same area, and culminating in the small community of Byron at the Wild Idol Inn. The result was three dead.

Deputy Attorney Michael Kalkstein, in his closing arguments, recounted the evidence presented by some forty witnesses and asked for a conviction of guilt. "They are both equally guilty no matter who you believe pulled the triggers. The cold-blooded, calculated execution of these people was committed after they were told to lie down on the floor with their heads on their hands. And then, with murder in their hearts, Jones and Gunther put the barrels of their guns to the backs of their heads and pulled the triggers. Those people never fought back; they never argued. They were killed in cold blood."

Jones and Gunther were acquitted of the kidnapping charge. They were found guilty of first-degree murder, burglary and robbery. After further delibera-tion, the jury handed down death-penalty verdicts for the two men.

As Jones and Gunther walked, shackled in leg irons, from the courtroom, there was no expression of emotion on their faces. They had showed no signs of regret during the trial.

But the words of the district attorney rang clear in the minds of those who sat through the seven-week trial. "It is a sad commen-tary on our times, when five men committing such

Virgil Gunther as taken under arrest by Tracy Chief of Police and Sherriff's Deputy [*John Wilson, Antioch Daily Ledger*]

serious and separate crimes as kidnapping and murder, should meet by coincidence at the only bar in a small town and leave behind them three people murdered in cold blood."

Afterword

Since the conviction and sentencing of Willis Jones and Virgil Gunther, Californians have abolished the death penalty and both are serving life sentences in prison. Todd Clair, because of his

Willis Jones (left) and Virgil Gunter (right) as they arrive handcuffed at the Contra Costa County Superior Court, Martinez, California [*The Concord Transcript, January 28, 1971*]

Vaught and Dean Sentenced 5 years to Life [*The Brentwood News, May 6, 1971, page 2*]

evidence and help in solving the crimes, plus the fact he was not involved in the kidnapping or murders, was given a light sentence and placed on probation. Billy Vaught and Jimmy Dean were sentenced to the state prison and are now out on parole.

Aftermath

Protagonists

The two felons are initially incarcerated and on death row, San Quentin State Prison. Each is transferred—upon commutation of their sentences—to life imprisonment with possibility of parole to separate California State Prisons. Willis Roy Jones, deceased in 2006, was transferred to Folsom State Prison. He died in Solano County and is buried in an unknown location. Virgil Albert Gunther was transferred to the California Men's Colony, San Louis Obispo. He was relocated to Valley State Prison in Chowchilla on Aug. 8, 2022—a Level II facility. He awaits a Parole Suitability Hearing in May 2024.

One of the three other protagonists involved in the *Coincidence* drama is James Dale Dean, who died in 1993 in Sutter County, and is buried in Oakhurst, California. The residence or life status of the remaining two men, Todd Clair and Billy Vaught, is unknown.

Victims

As for the Victims, Lloyd Wayne Young is buried at Oakview Cemetery in Antioch, California. He served in the Korea conflict during two enlistment periods in the U.S. Navy. He was a member of the Oglala Sioux Tribe. He left behind a wife, four children, his parents, and four siblings. Robert Austin Tracy was buried in Mono County. His wife Cecil M. Tracy is buried in Orange County.

Lloyd Young posing with sturgeon prior to 1969 [*Inside Detective Magazine,* Detective Publications, Inc., January 1971, Vol.49, No.1, pg. 18]

Owner

Pearl Kelso was quite a personality and civic-minded resident in East Contra Costa County. She married three times, raised her family here, plus owned and operated a tavern in Byron for 37 years. She moved to Byron in 1930 after 6 years of marriage to her first husband. She married Lou Crist in 1937. They purchased the Borden Junction Bar, a hunting and fishing hangout, located at the intersection of State Route 4 and the Byron-Bethany Road (J4). The property was sold in 1944. With the proceeds, they purchased both Rolando's in Brentwood and the Wild Idol Inn in Byron. Rolando's, renamed King's Corner, was subsequently sold and the couple moved out of the area. They returned to East Contra Costa County 5 years later and settled in Byron.

At the time the Crist's purchased the Wild Idol Inn, it was
known as Ray's Place. Local lore
holds that the bar was renamed
the Wild Idol after Lou's favorite
greyhound race dog. Lou died
in 1960, and Pearl married Bob
Kelso in 1964. She maintained
ownership and management of
the bar while her husband, Bob,
managed the Continental Club
in Brentwood. Pearl enjoyed
the business and clientele at the
Wild Idol Inn.

Pearl Kelso, owner of the Wild Idol
Inn at the time of the murders. [*The
Brentwood News*]

Pearl remembers Stanley
Pereira, the Sheriff at the time of the murders, helping at the bar.
The Byron Municipal Court, for which Pereira served as California's youngest judge, was located in the building next door. She also
remembers the Wild Idol Inn triple murders and the kidnapping
incident from the book *Coincidence*. Pearl kept the bar for four
more years after the murder incident, before finally selling and
retiring in 1974. During those four years, she hired a security guard
to come down at 2 a.m. every night at closing. She also personally,
went down each evening to make sure everything was safe and
secure for both patrons and property.

Pearl's third husband, Bob Kelso, preceded Pearl in death in
1982. Pearl Kelso has since died in 1996 (age 96) and buried in Union
Cemetery in Brentwood, California, Contra Costa County. She is
survived by two sons, Bill Jones Jr. and Jerald Crist, and several
grandchildren.

Survivor

David Spearman was the regular night bartender at the Wild Idol Inn. On this particular Saturday, his day job required swapping shifts with the Idol's regular day bartender.

Lucky circumstance or coincidence.

Spearman was returning home to Byron from work at around 2:30 a.m. and saw the lights still on at the Wild Idol Inn. He drove up to the bar, stopped his car and noticed the pool room shades were drawn. Window shades were never drawn at the bar. Something seemed amiss. He left his car, walked to the front door and reached to turn the knob. Instinct and suspicion stopped him. He

Interior of Wild Idol Saloon Pool Room, 2022 The shades were down when the regular night bartender, David Spearman, arrived at 2:30 a.m. [*Private Collection*]

Wild Idol Saloon, Main Street view, 2022 [*Private Collection*]

did not enter. Instead, David went home and called the bar. When no one answered, he called the sheriff. They were on their way.

Had David turned the knob to enter the Wild Idol Inn that night, he surely would not have lived to tell the tale.

MAGDALENA NORTHCUT

Interior view of the Wild Idol Saloon February, 2023 [*Private Collection*]

Interior view of the Wild Idol Saloon February, 2023 [*Private Collection*]

Behind Bars for 53 Years:
In Virgil Albert Gunther's Words

He was 22-years-old and destined to take his last breath on earth in the gas chamber in 1970, until a California law changed convicted killer and kidnapper, Virgil Albert Gunther's destiny.

While the abolished death penalty of Feb. 18, 1972—by a 6-1 vote on the California Supreme Court—might have spared Gunther his young life, it did not spare him from serving 53 years (and counting) in prison, mostly at the Men's Colony in San Luis Obispo. He was relocated to Valley State Prison in Chowchilla on Aug. 8, 2022— a Level II slammer. He is typically up for parole every five years and gets denied each time by protests from the survivors.

Collectable pin: California State Prison Men's Colony, San Luis Obispo County (1″ × .75″). The California Men's Colony is a male-only, minimum to medium security, correctional facility established in 1954

"Yes, I have been in prison for some time, and I know that I'll die behind bars," said the 75-year-old, in an Oct. 13,

---

2022, handwritten letter responding to a list of questions sent to the inmate via snail mail.

While in prison, the Porterville-born inmate has had lots of time to think.

"At least three or four times of my waking hours, I relive what lead up to that night," wrote Gunther.

He explained that there is a side to the murders no one wants to talk about—a side he said would clear him of the murder conviction—yet, no one wants to listen, he wrote.

Described here within the pages of *Coincidence*, Robert and Cecil Tracy, and Lloyd Young were murdered, execution-style, at the bar called Wild Idol Inn on Oct. 5, 1970 in Byron, by Willis Jones and Virgil Gunther. The double convictions do not specify who killed which victims and Gunther said he's never read the book. Jones is deceased and Gunther continues to carry out his sentence, with most likely, no chance at ever walking a free man on Earth.

"I have tried to get it out [his story] in the open, but there is no one that would help bring it into the light … but that is another story," he wrote. "I will pose a few questions that will cloud the waters, but it will do little to give me back my life."

He explained in his letters, "I have only the county's words of what happened, but in my own words, I still don't think that I was there."

Gunther explains the night of the triple homicide. It was his one-year anniversary with his wife, Sharon. The two were married in Reno on Oct. 5, 1969; she was 16, he was 22.

"That night I don't remember much … I do remember she [Sharon] handed me a drink and the next afternoon when I awoke, my landlord came over telling me about the Wild Idol Inn," wrote Gunther.

He continued, "There is nothing I could say to them I haven't said before. I feel for the family at their loss—I always did [for] Robert Tracy and Lloyd Young—I had never met Cecelia Tracy, but that still does not make me the killer."

When asked directly in one of the letters, if he killed the three victims, Gunther's answer is definitive.

"Simply no," he wrote. "I killed no one, but that's what all killers say ... that they killed no one. If it were a matter of money, I had an endorsed check in my wallet from a multi-millionaire, but that was taken and torn up by a San Joaquin County Sheriff Officer 'Beers.' So why would I have been out robbing and killing?"

Gunther states the multi-millionaire who gave him the signed, blank check, was his friend named Paul Ungeretti.

"He gave it to me, because he was a good friend," wrote Gunther. "Plus, he knew I would never use it if I didn't need it."

Part of the mystery, Gunther feels, lies with finding Ungeretti's grave.

"He too is gone [dead] now, if you wish, you could see if my plot is still next to his," wrote Gunther. "If you would find Paul's grave, it will come to light."

The survivor's family protests Gunther's release at every eligible parole date.

"If I were the one that killed their people, I could not blame them for their protest," wrote Gunther. "What does it matter at this late date—my life is shot to doll rags."

Virgil Albert Gunther, 2022 [*Virgil Gunther*]

Penitentiary life has not been easy, Gunther writes.

"Life in prison is not that great for the last, let's say, fifty years … it has been to keep my back to the wall, so it has not been a fun ride when you have staff lying about you and inmates that want your hide because you're white or brown or even Black or yellow," wrote Gunther. "The rule of thumb is—trust no one, so it's been kind of lonely for these 53 years."

Packages and letters come for Gunther in prison, sent to him by his family members, whom he says are older than him. He said he does not have contact with this daughter, named Donna, whom he says is 54-years-old now.

"She has no contact with me, except for a short visit at Soledad [Prison], when her mother was alive," wrote Gunther.

A life behind bars is not what Gunther wishes on anyone and wrote that he has spent much of his time helping other prison mates get their life together.

"I have helped prisoners with their problems and how to stay out of prison," he wrote. "To date, they now number close to 600 that have stayed out of prison, but I just give them the thoughts—it was up to them, so I had to make the best of [what] life dealt me."

Before prison, Gunther describes his life when he was young.

"A German kid growing up in a post-World War II [America] was bad enough, but being the son of the town drunk was not easy," he wrote.

Born in Porterville, California and raised in a small town called Poplar, outside of Porterville, Gunther, who successfully passed his

General Education Development ("GED") test in 1981 while behind bars, added, "So you can guess my life has been hell."

Looking back, Gunther contemplates what he could have done differently—if he could turn back time.

"Where to start?" he wrote. "Maybe I could have stayed in the womb and none of this would have ever happened—as my life was one you would not wish upon a dog. It would take 10 more [writing] tablets to explain what I mean."

"I had a nightmare that I was strapped into chair B and my so-called crime partner in chair A," wrote Gunther. "In the dream, I asked Jones, or told him, 'You could have spared me this' as the bitter ominous gas filled the room. I woke up in a cold sweat."

He continues, "Yeah, I could save my fishing partner's and my drinking partner's life, if I could roll back the time, and I would never have married Sharon, but that's another story."

Knowing his fate is most likely to remain behind bars, Gunther continues to agree to answer questions either by letter or timed phone calls.

"I tried to be as truthful as I could be—what have I got to gain—they're not going to release me to let me pet a dog or go fishing, so I'll just kick back and try to guide these young ones to a path that will keep them out of prison," wrote Gunther. "I teach them what to look for, so they don't get caught-up like I did."

Note from author and editor, Charleen Earley

I understand the sensitive and serious nature of everything described in Luckii Ludwig's book titled "Coincidence" and my written interviews with convicted murderer Virgil Albert Gunther. My heart goes out to the surviving families of the three murdered victims. Email address: CharleenBEarley@gmail.com.

Proprietor, Rich Hogan, and bartender, Jaime Dillard, welcome you back to the Wild Idol Saloon & Grill now open (January 28, 2023). Libations and good food every day. Freinds *[sic]* and Family come on down!

CPSIA information can be obtained
at www.ICGtesting.com
Printed in the USA
BVHW011053190423
662643BV00022B/988